Glencoe Mathematics

Algebra 2

Chapter 3
Resource Masters

McGraw Hill Glencoe

New York, New York   Columbus, Ohio   Chicago, Illinois   Peoria, Illinois   Woodland Hills, California

Consumable Workbooks Many of the worksheets contained in the Chapter Resource Masters are available as consumable workbooks in both English and Spanish.

	ISBN10	ISBN13
Study Guide and Intervention Workbook	0-07-877355-5	978-0-07-877355-6
Skills Practice Workbook	0-07-877357-1	978-0-07-877357-0
Practice Workbook	0-07-877358-X	978-0-07-877358-7
Word Problem Practice Workbook	0-07-877360-1	978-0-07-877360-0
Spanish Versions		
Study Guide and Intervention Workbook	0-07-877356-3	978-0-07-877356-3
Practice Workbook	0-07-877359-8	978-0-07-877359-4

Answers for Workbooks The answers for Chapter 3 of these workbooks can be found in the back of this Chapter Resource Masters booklet.

StudentWorks Plus™ This CD-ROM includes the entire Student Edition test along with the English workbooks listed above.

TeacherWorks Plus™ All of the materials found in this booklet are included for viewing, printing, and editing in this CD-ROM.

Spanish Assessment Masters (ISBN10: 0-07-877361-X, ISBN13: 978-0-07-877361-7)
These masters contain a Spanish version of Chapter 3 Test Form 2A and Form 2C.

 **Glencoe**

The **McGraw·Hill** Companies

Send all inquiries to:
Glencoe/McGraw-Hill
8787 Orion Place
Columbus, OH 43240

ISBN13: 978-0-07-873973-6
ISBN10: 0-07-873973-X

Algebra 2 CRM3

Printed in the United States of America

2 3 4 5 6 7 8 9 10 005 13 12 11 10 09 08 07

Contents

Teacher's Guide to Using the Chapter 3
Resource Masters .iv

Chapter Resources
Chapter 3 Student-Built Glossary 1
Chapter 3 Anticipation Guide (English) 3
Chapter 3 Anticipation Guide (Spanish) 4

Lesson 3-1
Solving Systems of Equations by Graphing
Lesson Reading Guide 5
Study Guide and Intervention 6
Skills Practice 8
Practice 9
Word Problem Practice 10
Enrichment 11
Spreadsheet Activity 12

Lesson 3-2
Solving Systems of Equations Algebraically
Lesson Reading Guide 13
Study Guide and Intervention 14
Skills Practice .16
Practice 17
Word Problem Practice 18
Enrichment 19

Lesson 3-3
Solving Systems of Inequalities by Graphing
Lesson Reading Guide 20
Study Guide and Intervention 21
Skills Practice .23
Practice 24
Word Problem Practice 25
Enrichment 26

Lesson 3-4
Linear Programming
Lesson Reading Guide 27
Study Guide and Intervention 28
Skills Practice .30
Practice 31
Word Problem Practice 32
Enrichment 33
Graphing Calculator Activity 34

Lesson 3-5
Solving Systems of Equations in Three Variables
Lesson Reading Guide 35
Study Guide and Intervention 36
Skills Practice .38
Practice 39
Word Problem Practice 40
Enrichment 41

Assessment
Student Recording Sheet 43
Rubric for Scoring Pre-AP 44
Chapter 3 Quizzes 1 and 2 45
Chapter 3 Quizzes 3 and 4 46
Chapter 3 Mid-Chapter Test 47
Chapter 3 Vocabulary Test 48
Chapter 3 Test, Form 1 49
Chapter 3 Test, Form 2A 51
Chapter 3 Test, Form 2B 53
Chapter 3 Test, Form 2C 55
Chapter 3 Test, Form 2D 57
Chapter 3 Test, Form 3 59
Chapter 3 Extended Response Test 61
Standardized Test Practice 62

Answers A1–A34

Teacher's Guide to Using the
Chapter 3 Resource Masters

The *Chapter 3 Resource Masters* includes the core materials needed for Chapter 3. These materials include worksheets, extensions, and assessment options. The answers for these pages appear at the back of this booklet.

All of the materials found in this booklet are included for viewing and printing on the *TeacherWorks Plus*™ CD-ROM.

Chapter Resources

Student-Built Glossary (pages 1–2) These masters are a student study tool that presents up to twenty of the key vocabulary terms from the chapter. Students are to record definitions and/or examples for each term. You may suggest that students highlight or star the terms with which they are not familiar. Give this to students before beginning Lesson 3-1. Encourage them to add these pages to their mathematics study notebooks. Remind them to complete the appropriate words as they study each lesson.

Anticipation Guide (pages 3–4) This master, presented in both English and Spanish, is a survey used before beginning the chapter to pinpoint what students may or may not know about the concepts in the chapter. Students will revisit this survey after they complete the chapter to see if their perceptions have changed.

Lesson Resources

Lesson Reading Guide Get Ready for the Lesson extends the discussion from the beginning of the Student Edition lesson. Read the Lesson asks students to interpret the context of and relationships among terms in the lesson. Finally, Remember What You Learned asks students to summarize what they have learned using various representation techniques. Use as a study tool for note taking or as an informal reading assignment. It is also a helpful tool for ELL (English Language Learners).

Study Guide and Intervention These masters provide vocabulary, key concepts, additional worked-out examples and Check Your Progress exercises to use as a reteaching activity. It can also be used in conjunction with the Student Edition as an instructional tool for students who have been absent.

Skills Practice This master focuses more on the computational nature of the lesson. Use as an additional practice option or as homework for second-day teaching of the lesson.

Practice This master closely follows the types of problems found in the Exercises section of the Student Edition and includes word problems. Use as an additional practice option or as homework for second-day teaching of the lesson.

Word Problem Practice This master includes additional practice in solving word problems that apply the concepts of the lesson. Use as an additional practice or as homework for second-day teaching of the lesson.

Enrichment These activities may extend the concepts of the lesson, offer an historical or multicultural look at the concepts, or widen students' perspectives on the mathematics they are learning. They are written for use with all levels of students.

Graphing Calculator, Scientific Calculator, or Spreadsheet Activities

These activities present ways in which technology can be used with the concepts in some lessons of this chapter. Use as an alternative approach to some concepts or as an integral part of your lesson presentation.

Assessment Options

The assessment masters in the *Chapter 3 Resource Masters* offer a wide range of assessment tools for formative (monitoring) assessment and summative (final) assessment.

Student Recording Sheet This master corresponds with the standardized test practice at the end of the chapter.

Pre-AP Rubric This master provides information for teachers and students on how to assess performance on open-ended questions.

Quizzes Four free-response quizzes offer assessment at appropriate intervals in the chapter.

Mid-Chapter Test This 1-page test provides an option to assess the first half of the chapter. It parallels the timing of the Mid-Chapter Quiz in the Student Edition and includes both multiple-choice and free-response questions.

Vocabulary Test This test is suitable for all students. It includes a list of vocabulary words and 10 questions to assess students' knowledge of those words. This can also be used in conjunction with one of the leveled chapter tests.

Leveled Chapter Tests

- *Form 1* contains multiple-choice questions and is intended for use with below grade level students.

- *Forms 2A and 2B* contain multiple-choice questions aimed at on grade level students. These tests are similar in format to offer comparable testing situations.

- *Forms 2C and 2D* contain free-response questions aimed at on grade level students. These tests are similar in format to offer comparable testing situations.

- *Form 3* is a free-response test for use with above grade level students.

All of the above mentioned tests include a free-response Bonus question.

Extended-Response Test Performance assessment tasks are suitable for all students. Sample answers and a scoring rubric are included for evaluation.

Standardized Test Practice These three pages are cumulative in nature. It includes three parts: multiple-choice questions with bubble-in answer format, griddable questions with answer grids, and short-answer free-response questions.

Answers

- The answers for the Anticipation Guide and Lesson Resources are provided as reduced pages with answers appearing in red.

- Full-size answer keys are provided for the assessment masters.

3   Student-Built Glossary

This is an alphabetical list of the key vocabulary terms you will learn in Chapter 3. As you study the chapter, complete each term's definition or description. Remember to add the page number where you found the term. Add these pages to your Algebra Study Notebook to review vocabulary at the end of the chapter.

Vocabulary Term	Found on Page	Definition/Description/Example
bounded region		
consistent system		
constraints (kuhn·STRAYNTS)		
dependent system		
elimination method		
feasible (FEE·zuh·buhl) region		
inconsistent (ihn·kuhn·SIHS·tuhnt) system		
independent system		

(continued on the next page)

3   **Student-Built Glossary**

Vocabulary Term	Found on Page	Definition/Description/Example
linear programming		
ordered triple		
substitution method		
system of equations		
system of inequalities		
unbounded region		
vertex		

3 Anticipation Guide

Systems of Equations and Inequalities

STEP 1 *Before you begin Chapter 3*

- Read each statement.

- Decide whether you Agree (A) or Disagree (D) with the statement.

- Write A or D in the first column OR if you are not sure whether you agree or disagree, write NS (Not Sure).

STEP 1 A, D, or NS	Statement	STEP 2 A or D
	1. A system of equations consists of two or more equations with different variables.	
	2. The solution of a system of equations can be found by finding the intersection of the graphs of the equations.	
	3. A system of equations that is inconsistent has an infinite number of solutions.	
	4. Given the two equations $y = x - 7$ and $3x + 4y = 10$, a solution can be found by substituting $x - 7$ for y in the second equation.	
	5. The product of the equation $6m - 4n = 22$ and -2 is $-12m + 8n = 22$.	
	6. When solving a system of inequalities by graphing, if the graphs do not intersect then there is no solution.	
	7. All the ordered pairs in the intersection of the graphs of a system of inequalities are called constraints.	
	8. If the intersection of the graphs of a system of inequalities is a polygonal region, that region is called bounded.	
	9. Linear programming is the process of finding all solutions to a system of linear inequalities.	
	10. The solution to a system of equations with three variables is written as (x, y, z) and is called an ordered triple.	

STEP 2 *After you complete Chapter 3*

- Reread each statement and complete the last column by entering an A or a D.

- Did any of your opinions about the statements change from the first column?

- For those statements that you mark with a D, use a piece of paper to write an example of why you disagree.

Chapter Resources

3 ⟩ Ejercicios preparatorios

Sistemas de ecuaciones y desigualdades

PASO 1   *Antes de comenzar el Capítulo 3*

- Lee cada enunciado.

- Decide si estás de acuerdo (A) o en desacuerdo (D) con el enunciado.

- Escribe A o D en la primera columna O si no estás seguro(a) de la respuesta, escribe NS (No estoy seguro(a).

PASO 1 A, D o NS	Enunciado	PASO 2 A o D
	1. Un sistema de ecuaciones consta de dos o más ecuaciones con diferentes variables.	
	2. La solución de un sistema de ecuaciones se calcula al hallar la intersección de las gráficas de las ecuaciones.	
	3. Un sistema de ecuaciones inconsistente tiene un número infinito de soluciones.	
	4. Dadas las dos ecuaciones $y = x - 7$ y $3x + 4y = 10$, se puede calcular una solución reemplazando $x - 7$ por y en la segunda ecuación.	
	5. El producto de la ecuación $6m - 4n = 22$ por -2 es $-12m + 8n = 22$.	
	6. Al resolver un sistema de desigualdades con gráficas, si las gráficas no se intersecan, entonces éste no tiene solución.	
	7. Todos los pares ordenados en la intersección de las gráficas de un sistema de desigualdades se llaman restricciones.	
	8. Si la intersección de las gráficas de un sistema de desigualdades es una región poligonal, se dice que esa región está acotada.	
	9. La programación lineal es el proceso de hallar todas las soluciones a un sistema de desigualdades lineales.	
	10. La solución a un sistema de ecuaciones con tres variables se escribe en la forma (x, y, z) y se llama triple ordenado.	

PASO 2   *Después de completar el Capítulo 3*

- Vuelve a leer cada enunciado y completa la última columna con una A o una D.

- ¿Cambió cualquiera de tus opiniones sobre los enunciados de la primera columna?

- En una hoja de papel aparte, escribe un ejemplo de por qué estás en desacuerdo con los enunciados que marcaste con una D.

3-1 **Lesson Reading Guide**

Solving Systems of Equations by Graphing

Get Ready for the Lesson

Read the introduction to Lesson 3-1 in your textbook.

• Which are growing faster, in-store sales or online sales?

• In what year is the in-store and online sales the same?

Read the Lesson

1. The Study Tip on page 117 of your textbook says that when you solve a system of equations by graphing and find a point of intersection of the two lines, you must always check the ordered pair in *both* of the original equations. Why is it not good enough to check the ordered pair in just one of the equations?

2. Under each system graphed below, write all of the following words that apply: *consistent*, *inconsistent*, *dependent*, and *independent*.

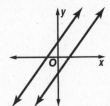   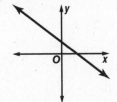   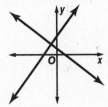

Remember What You Learned

3. Look up the words *consistent* and *inconsistent* in a dictionary. How can the meaning of these words help you distinguish between consistent and inconsistent systems of equations?

3-1 Study Guide and Intervention

Solving Systems of Equations by Graphing

Graph Systems of Equations A system of equations is a set of two or more equations containing the same variables. You can solve a system of linear equations by graphing the equations on the same coordinate plane. If the lines intersect, the solution is that intersection point.

Example **Solve the system of equations by graphing.** $x - 2y = 4$
$x + y = -2$

Write each equation in slope-intercept form.

$x - 2y = 4 \quad \rightarrow \quad y = \dfrac{x}{2} - 2$

$x + y = -2 \quad \rightarrow \quad y = -x - 2$

The graphs appear to intersect at $(0, -2)$.

CHECK Substitute the coordinates into each equation.

$$\begin{array}{ll} x - 2y = 4 & x + y = -2 \\ 0 - 2(-2) \stackrel{?}{=} 4 & 0 + (-2) \stackrel{?}{=} -2 \\ 4 = 4 \checkmark & -2 = -2 \checkmark \end{array}$$

The solution of the system is $(0, -2)$.

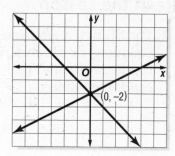

Exercises

Solve each system of equations by graphing.

1. $y = -\dfrac{x}{3} + 1$

$y = \dfrac{x}{2} - 4$

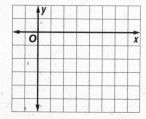

2. $y = 2x - 2$

$y = -x + 4$

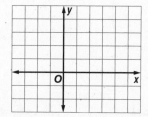

3. $y = -\dfrac{x}{2} + 3$

$y = \dfrac{x}{4}$

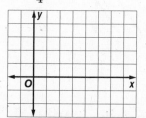

4. $3x - y = 0$

$x - y = -2$

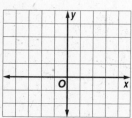

5. $2x + \dfrac{y}{3} = -7$

$\dfrac{x}{2} + y = 1$

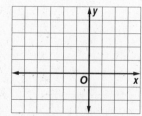

6. $\dfrac{x}{2} - y = 2$

$2x - y = -1$

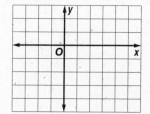

3-1 Study Guide and Intervention (continued)

Solving Systems of Equations by Graphing

Classify Systems of Equations The following chart summarizes the possibilities for graphs of two linear equations in two variables.

Graphs of Equations	Slopes of Lines	Classification of System	Number of Solutions
Lines intersect	Different slopes	Consistent and independent	One
Lines coincide (same line)	Same slope, same y-intercept	Consistent and dependent	Infinitely many
Lines are parallel	Same slope, different y-intercepts	Inconsistent	None

Example Graph the system of equations and describe it as *consistent and independent*, *consistent and dependent*, or *inconsistent*.

$$x - 3y = 6$$
$$2x - y = -3$$

Write each equation in slope-intercept form.

$$x - 3y = 6 \quad \rightarrow \quad y = \frac{1}{3}x - 2$$
$$2x - y = -3 \quad \rightarrow \quad y = 2x + 3$$

The graphs intersect at $(-3, -3)$. Since there is one solution, the system is consistent and independent.

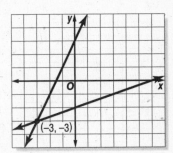

Exercises

Graph the system of equations and describe it as *consistent and independent*, *consistent and dependent*, or *inconsistent*.

1. $3x + y = -2$
$6x + 2y = 10$

2. $x + 2y = 5$
$3x - 15 = -6y$

3. $2x - 3y = 0$
$4x - 6y = 3$

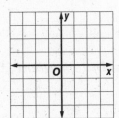
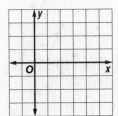
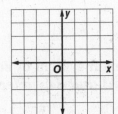

4. $2x - y = 3$
$x + 2y = 4$

5. $4x + y = -2$
$2x + \dfrac{y}{2} = -1$

6. $3x - y = 2$
$x + y = 6$

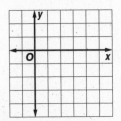
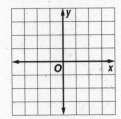
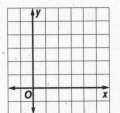

Lesson 3-1

3-1 Skills Practice

Solving Systems of Equations By Graphing

Solve each system of equations by graphing.

1. $x = 2$
   $y = 0$

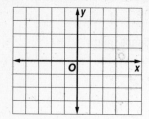

2. $y = -3x + 6$
   $y = 2x - 4$

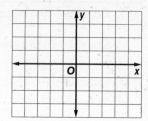

3. $y = 4 - 3x$
   $y = -\frac{1}{2}x - 1$

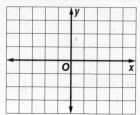

4. $y = 4 - x$
   $y = x - 2$

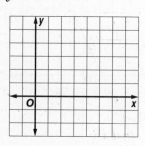

5. $y = -2x + 2$
   $y = \frac{1}{3}x - 5$

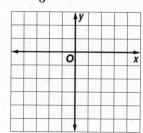

6. $y = x$
   $y = -3x + 4$

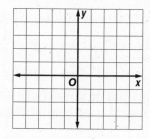

7. $x + y = 3$
   $x - y = 1$

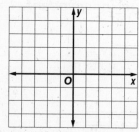

8. $x - y = 4$
   $2x - 5y = 8$

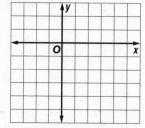

9. $3x - 2y = 4$
   $2x - y = 1$

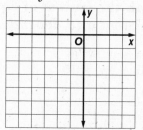

Graph each system of equations and describe it as *consistent and independent*, *consistent and dependent*, or *inconsistent*.

10. $y = -3x$
    $y = -3x + 2$

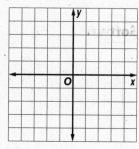

11. $y = x - 5$
    $-2x + 2y = -10$

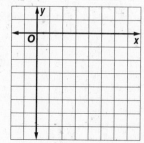

12. $2x - 5y = 10$
    $3x + y = 15$

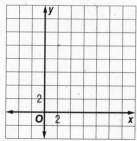

3-1 Practice

Solving Systems of Equations By Graphing

Solve each system of equations by graphing.

1. $x - 2y = 0$
$y = 2x - 3$

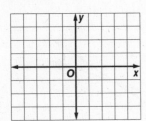

2. $x + 2y = 4$
$2x - 3y = 1$

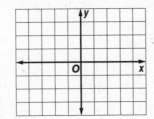

3. $2x + y = 3$
$y = \frac{1}{2}x - \frac{9}{2}$

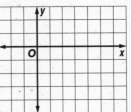

4. $y - x = 3$
$y = 1$

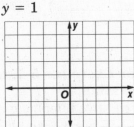

5. $2x - y = 6$
$x + 2y = -2$

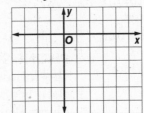

6. $5x - y = 4$
$-2x + 6y = 4$

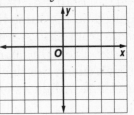

Graph each system of equations and describe it as *consistent and independent*, *consistent and dependent*, or *inconsistent*.

7. $2x - y = 4$
$x - y = 2$

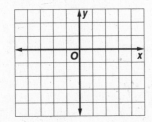

8. $y = -x - 2$
$x + y = -4$

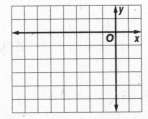

9. $2y - 8 = x$
$y = \frac{1}{2}x + 4$

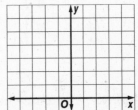

SOFTWARE For Exercises 10–12, use the following information.

Location Mapping needs new software. Software A costs $13,000 plus $500 per additional site license. Software B costs $2500 plus $1200 per additional site license.

10. Write two equations that represent the cost of each software.

11. Graph the equations. Estimate the break-even point of the software costs.

12. If Location Mapping plans to buy 10 additional site licenses, which software will cost less?

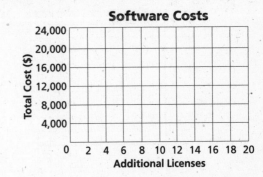

9

Lesson 3-1

3-1 Word Problem Practice

Solving Systems of Equations By Graphing

1. **STREETS** Andrew is studying a map and notices two streets that run parallel to each other. He computes the equations of the lines that represent the two roads. Are these two equations *consistent* or *inconsistent*? If they are consistent, are they *independent* or *dependent*? Explain.

2. **SPOTLIGHTS** Ship A has coordinates $(-1, -2)$ and Ship B has coordinates $(-4, 1)$. Both ships have their spotlights fixated on the same lifeboat. The light beam from Ship A travels along the line $y = 2x$. The light beam from Ship B travels along the line $y = x + 5$. What are the coordinates of the lifeboat?

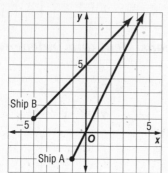

3. **LASERS** A machine heats up a single point by shining several lasers at it. The equations $y = x + 1$ and $y = -x + 7$ describe two of the laser beams. Graph both of these lines to find the coordinates of the heated point

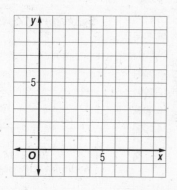

4. **PATHS** The graph shows the paths of two people who took a walk in a park. Where did their paths intersect?

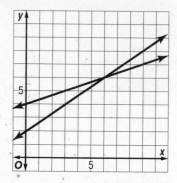

PHONE SERVICE For Exercises 5–7, use the following information.
Beth is deciding between two telephone plans. Plan A charges $15 per month plus 10 cents per minute. Plan B charges $20 per month plus 5 cents per minute.

5. Write a system of equations that represent the monthly cost of each plan.

6. Graph the equations.

7. For how many minutes per month do the two phone plans cost the same amount?

3-1   Enrichment

Solutions to Nonlinear Equations

Real-life situations are often not capable of being represented by a linear equation. Systems of nonlinear equations are often used in the study of population dynamics, modeling carbon monoxide exposure, and determining the height of an object in free fall.

Nonlinear equations have one variable raised to a power other than one or multiplication of two or more variables.

> **Examples**

a. $xy = 1$ or $y = \dfrac{1}{x}$ The first equation has a product of two variables.
The second is the same equation solved for y.

b. $y = x^3 - 2x + 1$ The variable x is raised to the third power.

Systems of nonlinear equations consist of two or more equations, where at least one is nonlinear.

Solutions to these systems are typically difficult to find. One useful method for finding solutions to systems of nonlinear equations is the same as the method for finding solutions to systems of linear equations—use technology to graph the system and find the point(s) of intersection. The graph of the system is shown at the right.

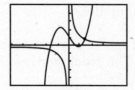

$$\begin{cases} y = \dfrac{1}{x} \\ y = x^3 - 2x + 1 \end{cases}$$

Using the Intersection function of a graphing calculator you find that one point of intersection is approximately (1.34509, 0.743445).

> **Exercises**

1. Use a graphing calculator to find the other point of intersection.

2. Use the **Zoom** feature on the calculator to zoom in around the point of intersection. What do the two nonlinear equations remind you of at this level of zoom?

3. GOLF The height of a golf ball dropped from the top of a 100-foot tower after t seconds is given by $h = -16t^3 + 100$. Use a graphing calculator to determine when (in seconds) the golf ball is 10 feet from the ground.

3-1 Spreadsheet Activity

Break-Even Point

You have learned that the break-even point is the point at which the income equals the cost. You can use the formulas and charts in a spreadsheet to find a break-even point.

Example Carly Ericson is considering opening a candle business. She estimates that she will have an annual overhead of $15,000. It costs Carly $3.00 to make a jar candle, which she sells for $12.50. What is Carly's break-even point?

Use Column A for the number of candles. Columns B and C are the cost and the income, respectively.

Extend the rows of the spreadsheet to find the point at which the income first exceeds the cost. The break-even point occurs between this point and the previous point. In this case, the break even point occurs between 1500 and 1600 candles.

The chart tool of the spreadsheet allows you to graph the data. The graph verifies the solution.

	A	B	C
1	Candles	Cost	Income
2	0	$15,000	$0
3	100	$15,300	$1,250
4	200	$15,600	$2,500
5	300	$15,900	$3,750
6	400	$16,200	$5,000
7	500	$16,500	$6,250
8	600	$16,800	$7,500
9	700	$17,100	$8,750
10	800	$17,400	$10,000
11	900	$17,700	$11,250
12	1000	$18,000	$12,500
13	1100	$18,300	$13,750
14	1200	$18,600	$15,000
15	1300	$18,900	$16,250
16	1400	$19,200	$17,500
17	1500	$19,500	$18,750
18	1600	$19,800	$20,000

Sheet 1 | Sheet 2 | Sheet 3

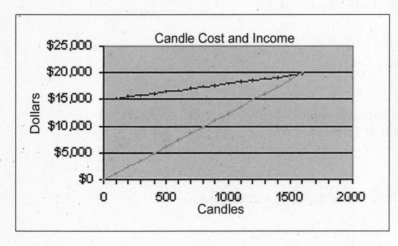

Exercises

1. If Carly could decrease her annual overhead to $14,000, what would the break-even point be?

2. Suppose Carly decreases her annual overhead to $14,000 and increases the price of a candle to $14.00. What is the new break-even point?

3-2 Lesson Reading Guide

Solving Systems of Equations Algebraically

Get Ready for the Lesson

Read the introduction to Lesson 3-2 in your textbook.

- How many more minutes of long distance time did Yolanda use in February than in January?

- How much more were the February charges than the January charges?

- Using your answers for the questions above, how can you find the rate per minute?

Read the Lesson

1. Suppose that you are asked to solve the system of equations at the right by the substitution method.

$$4x - 5y = 7$$
$$3x + y = -9$$

The first step is to solve one of the equations for one variable in terms of the other. To make your work as easy as possible, which equation would you solve for which variable? Explain.

2. Suppose that you are asked to solve the system of equations at the right by the elimination method.

$$2x + 3y = -2$$
$$7x - y = 39$$

To make your work as easy as possible, which variable would you eliminate? Describe how you would do this.

Remember What You Learned

3. The substitution method and elimination method for solving systems both have several steps, and it may be difficult to remember them. You may be able to remember them more easily if you notice what the methods have in common. What step is the same in both methods?

3-2 Study Guide and Intervention

Solving Systems of Equations Algebraically

Substitution To solve a system of linear equations by **substitution**, first solve for one variable in terms of the other in one of the equations. Then substitute this expression into the other equation and simplify.

Example Use substitution to solve the system of equations. $2x - y = 9$
$x + 3y = -6$

Solve the first equation for y in terms of x.

$2x - y = 9$	First equation
$-y = -2x + 9$	Subtract $2x$ from both sides.
$y = 2x - 9$	Multiply both sides by -1.

Substitute the expression $2x - 9$ for y into the second equation and solve for x.

$x + 3y = -6$	Second equation
$x + 3(2x - 9) = -6$	Substitute $2x - 9$ for y.
$x + 6x - 27 = -6$	Distributive Property
$7x - 27 = -6$	Simplify.
$7x = 21$	Add 27 to each side.
$x = 3$	Divide each side by 7.

Now, substitute the value 3 for x in either original equation and solve for y.

$2x - y = 9$	First equation
$2(3) - y = 9$	Replace x with 3.
$6 - y = 9$	Simplify.
$-y = 3$	Subtract 6 from each side.
$y = -3$	Multiply each side by -1.

The solution of the system is $(3, -3)$.

Exercises

Solve each system of linear equations by using substitution.

1. $3x + y = 7$
$4x + 2y = 16$

2. $2x + y = 5$
$3x - 3y = 3$

3. $2x + 3y = -3$
$x + 2y = 2$

4. $2x - y = 7$
$6x - 3y = 14$

5. $4x - 3y = 4$
$2x + y = -8$

6. $5x + y = 6$
$3 - x = 0$

7. $x + 8y = -2$
$x - 3y = 20$

8. $2x - y = -4$
$4x + y = 1$

9. $x - y = -2$
$2x - 3y = 2$

10. $x - 4y = 4$
$2x + 12y = 13$

11. $x + 3y = 2$
$4x + 12y = 8$

12. $2x + 2y = 4$
$x - 2y = 0$

3-2 Study Guide and Intervention (continued)

Solving Systems of Equations Algebraically

Elimination To solve a system of linear equations by **elimination**, add or subtract the equations to eliminate one of the variables. You may first need to multiply one or both of the equations by a constant so that one of the variables has the same (or opposite) coefficient in one equation as it has in the other.

Example 1 Use the elimination method to solve the system of equations.

$2x - 4y = -26$
$3x - y = -24$

Multiply the second equation by 4. Then subtract the equations to eliminate the y variable.

$2x - 4y = -26$
$3x - y = -24$ Multiply by 4.

$\begin{array}{rcl} 2x - 4y &=& -26 \\ 12x - 4y &=& -96 \\ \hline -10x &=& 70 \\ x &=& -7 \end{array}$

Replace x with -7 and solve for y.
$2x - 4y = -26$
$2(-7) - 4y = -26$
$-14 - 4y = -26$
$-4y = -12$
$y = 3$
The solution is $(-7, 3)$.

Example 2 Use the elimination method to solve the system of equations.

$3x - 2y = 4$
$5x + 3y = -25$

Multiply the first equation by 3 and the second equation by 2. Then add the equations to eliminate the y variable.

$3x - 2y = 4$ Multiply by 3.
$5x + 3y = -25$ Multiply by 2.

$\begin{array}{rcl} 9x - 6y &=& 12 \\ 10x + 6y &=& -50 \\ \hline 19x &=& -38 \\ x &=& -2 \end{array}$

Replace x with -2 and solve for y.
$3x - 2y = 4$
$3(-2) - 2y = 4$
$-6 - 2y = 4$
$-2y = 10$
$y = -5$
The solution is $(-2, -5)$.

Exercises

Solve each system of equations by using elimination.

1. $2x - y = 7$
$3x + y = 8$

2. $x - 2y = 4$
$-x + 6y = 12$

3. $3x + 4y = -10$
$x - 4y = 2$

4. $3x - y = 12$
$5x + 2y = 20$

5. $4x - y = 6$
$2x - \dfrac{y}{2} = 4$

6. $5x + 2y = 12$
$-6x - 2y = -14$

7. $2x + y = 8$
$3x + \dfrac{3}{2}y = 12$

8. $7x + 2y = -1$
$4x - 3y = -13$

9. $3x + 8y = -6$
$x - y = 9$

10. $5x + 4y = 12$
$7x - 6y = 40$

11. $-4x + y = -12$
$4x + 2y = 6$

12. $5m + 2n = -8$
$4m + 3n = 2$

Lesson 3-2

3-2 Skills Practice

Solving Systems of Equations Algebraically

Solve each system of equations by using substitution.

1. $m + n = 20$
$m - n = -4$

2. $x + 3y = -3$
$4x + 3y = 6$

3. $w - z = 1$
$2w + 3z = 12$

4. $3r + s = 5$
$2r - s = 5$

5. $2b + 3c = -4$
$b + c = 3$

6. $x - y = -5$
$3x + 4y = 13$

Solve each system of equations by using elimination.

7. $2p - q = 17$
$3p + q = 8$

8. $2j - k = 3$
$3j + k = 2$

9. $3c - 2d = 2$
$3c + 4d = 50$

10. $2f + 3g = 9$
$f - g = 2$

11. $-2x + y = -1$
$x + 2y = 3$

12. $2x - y = 12$
$2x - y = 6$

Solve each system of equations by using either substitution or elimination.

13. $-r + t = 5$
$-2r + t = 4$

14. $2x - y = -5$
$4x + y = 2$

15. $x - 3y = -12$
$2x + y = 11$

16. $2p - 3q = 6$
$-2p + 3q = -6$

17. $6w - 8z = 16$
$3w - 4z = 8$

18. $c + d = 6$
$c - d = 0$

19. $2u + 4v = -6$
$u + 2v = 3$

20. $3a + b = -1$
$-3a + b = 5$

21. $2x + y = 6$
$3x - 2y = 16$

22. $3y - z = -6$
$-3y - z = 6$

23. $c + 2d = -2$
$-2c - 5d = 3$

24. $3r - 2s = 1$
$2r - 3s = 9$

25. The sum of two numbers is 12. The difference of the same two numbers is -4. Find the numbers.

26. Twice a number minus a second number is -1. Twice the second number added to three times the first number is 9. Find the two numbers.

3-2 Practice

Solving Systems of Equations Algebraically

Solve each system of equations by using substitution.

1. $2x + y = 4$
$3x + 2y = 1$

2. $x - 3y = 9$
$x + 2y = -1$

3. $g + 3h = 8$
$\frac{1}{3}g + h = 9$

4. $2a - 4b = 6$
$-a + 2b = -3$

5. $2m + n = 6$
$5m + 6n = 1$

6. $4x - 3y = -6$
$-x - 2y = 7$

7. $u - 2v = \frac{1}{2}$
$-u + 2v = 5$

8. $x - 3y = 16$
$4x - y = 9$

9. $w + 3z = 1$
$3w - 5z = -4$

Solve each system of equations by using elimination.

10. $2r + s = 5$
$3r - s = 20$

11. $2m - n = -1$
$3m + 2n = 30$

12. $6x + 3y = 6$
$8x + 5y = 12$

13. $3j - k = 10$
$4j - k = 16$

14. $2x - y = -4$
$-4x + 2y = 6$

15. $2g + h = 6$
$3g - 2h = 16$

16. $2t + 4v = 6$
$-t - 2v = -3$

17. $3x - 2y = 12$
$2x + \frac{2}{3}y = 14$

18. $\frac{1}{2}x + 3y = 11$
$8x - 5y = 17$

Solve each system of equations by using either substitution or elimination.

19. $8x + 3y = -5$
$10x + 6y = -13$

20. $8q - 15r = -40$
$4q + 2r = 56$

21. $3x - 4y = 12$
$\frac{1}{3}x - \frac{4}{9}y = \frac{4}{3}$

22. $4b - 2d = 5$
$-2b + d = 1$

23. $s + 3y = 4$
$s = 1$

24. $4m - 2p = 0$
$-3m + 9p = 5$

25. $5g + 4k = 10$
$-3g - 5k = 7$

26. $0.5x + 2y = 5$
$x - 2y = -8$

27. $h - z = 3$
$-3h + 3z = 6$

SPORTS For Exercises 28 and 29, use the following information.

Last year the volleyball team paid $5 per pair for socks and $17 per pair for shorts on a total purchase of $315. This year they spent $342 to buy the same number of pairs of socks and shorts because the socks now cost $6 a pair and the shorts cost $18.

28. Write a system of two equations that represents the number of pairs of socks and shorts bought each year.

29. How many pairs of socks and shorts did the team buy each year?

Lesson 3-2

3-2 **Word Problem Practice**
Solving Systems of Equations Algebraically

1. **SUPPLIES** Kirsta and Arthur both need pens and blank CDs. The equation that represents Kirsta's purchases is $y = 27 - 3x$. The equation that represents Arthur's purchases is $y = 17 - x$. If x represents the price of the pens, and y represents the price of the CDs, what are the prices of the pens and the CDs?

2. **WALKING** Amy is walking a straight path that can be represented by the equation $y = 2x + 3$. At the same time Kendra is walking the straight path that has the equation $3y = 6x + 6$. What is the solution to the system of equations that represents the paths the two girls walked? Explain.

3. **CAFETERIA** To furnish a cafeteria, a school can spend $5200 on tables and chairs. Tables cost $200 and chairs cost $40. Each table will have 8 chairs around it. How many tables and chairs will the school purchase?

4. **PRICES** At a store, toothbrushes cost x dollars and bars of soap cost y dollars. One customer bought 2 toothbrushes and 1 bar of soap for $11. Another customer bought 6 toothbrushes and 5 bars of soap for $38. Both amounts do not include tax. Write and solve a system of equations for x and y.

GAMES For Exercises 5–7, use the following information.
Mark and Stephanie are playing a game where they toss a dart at a game board that is hanging on the wall. The points earned from a toss depends on where the dart lands. The center area is worth more points than the surrounding area. Each player tosses 12 darts.

5. Stephanie earned a total of 66 points with 6 darts landing in each area. Mark earned a total of 56 points with 4 darts landing in the center area, and 8 darts landing in the surrounding area. Write a system of equations that represents the number of darts each player tossed into each section. Use x for the inner circle, and y for the outer circle.

6. How many points is the inner circle worth? How many points is the outer circle worth?

7. If a player gets 10 darts in the inner circle and 2 in the outer circle the total score is doubled. How many points would the player earn if he or she gets exactly 10 darts in the center?

3-2 Enrichment

Using Coordinates

From one observation point, the line of sight to a downed plane is given by $y = x - 1$. This equation describes the distance from the observation point to the plane in a straight line. From another observation point, the line of sight is given by $x + 3y = 21$. What are the coordinates of the point at which the crash occurred?

Solve the system of equations $\begin{cases} y = x - 1 \\ x + 3y = 21 \end{cases}$.

$x + 3y = 21$
$x + 3(x - 1) = 21$ Substitute $x - 1$ for y.
$x + 3x - 3 = 21$
$4x = 24$
$x = 6$

$x + 3y = 21$
$6 + 3y = 21$ Substitute 6 for x.
$3y = 15$
$y = 5$

The coordinates of the crash are $(6, 5)$.

Solve.

1. The lines of sight to a forest fire are as follows.

   From Ranger Station A: $3x + y = 9$
   From Ranger Station B: $2x + 3y = 13$
   Find the coordinates of the fire.

2. An airplane is traveling along the line $x - y = -1$ when it sees another airplane traveling along the line $5x + 3y = 19$. If they continue along the same lines, at what point will their flight paths cross?

3. Two mine shafts are dug along the paths of the following equations.

   $x - y = 1400$
   $2x + y = 1300$

   If the shafts meet at a depth of 200 feet, what are the coordinates of the point at which they meet?

Lesson 3-2

3-3 Lesson Reading Guide

Solving Systems of Inequalities by Graphing

Get Ready for the Lesson

Read the introduction to Lesson 3-3 in your textbook.

Satish is 37 years old. He has a blood pressure reading of 135/99. Is his blood pressure within the normal range? Explain.

Read the Lesson

1. Without actually drawing the graph, describe the boundary lines for the system of inequalities shown at the right.

$$|x| < 3$$
$$|y| \leq 5$$

2. Think about how the graph would look for the system given above. What will be the shape of the shaded region? (It is not necessary to draw the graph. See if you can imagine it without drawing anything. If this is difficult to do, make a rough sketch to help you answer the question.)

3. Which system of inequalities matches the graph shown at the right?

   A. $x - y \leq -2$
   $x - y > 2$

   B. $x - y \geq -2$
   $x - y < 2$

   C. $x + y \leq -2$
   $x + y > 2$

   D. $x - y > -2$
   $x - y \leq 2$

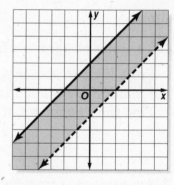

Remember What You Learned

4. To graph a system of inequalities, you must graph two or more boundary lines. When you graph each of these lines, how can the inequality symbols help you remember whether to use a dashed or solid line?

3-3 Study Guide and Intervention

Solving Systems of Inequalities by Graphing

Graph Systems of Inequalities To solve a system of inequalities, graph the inequalities in the same coordinate plane. The solution set is represented by the intersection of the graphs.

Example Solve the system of inequalities by graphing.

$y \leq 2x - 1$ and $y > \dfrac{x}{3} + 2$

The solution of $y \leq 2x - 1$ is Regions 1 and 2.

The solution of $y > \dfrac{x}{3} + 2$ is Regions 1 and 3.

The intersection of these regions is Region 1, which is the solution set of the system of inequalities.

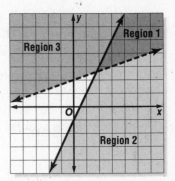

Exercises

Solve each system of inequalities by graphing.

1. $x - y \leq 2$
$x + 2y \geq 1$

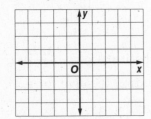

2. $3x - 2y \leq -1$
$x + 4y \geq -12$

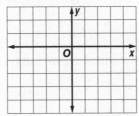

3. $|y| \leq 1$
$x > 2$

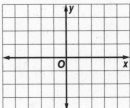

4. $y \geq \dfrac{x}{2} - 3$
$y < 2x$

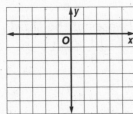

5. $y < \dfrac{x}{3} + 2$
$y < -2x + 1$

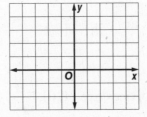

6. $y \geq -\dfrac{x}{4} + 1$
$y < 3x - 1$

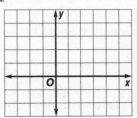

7. $x + y \geq 4$
$2x - y > 2$

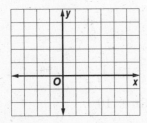

8. $x + 3y < 3$
$x - 2y \geq 4$

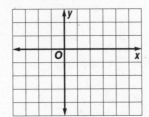

9. $x - 2y > 6$
$x + 4y < -4$

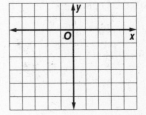

Lesson 3-3

3-3 Study Guide and Intervention (continued)

Solving Systems of Inequalities by Graphing

Find Vertices of a Polygonal Region Sometimes the graph of a system of inequalities forms a bounded region. You can find the vertices of the region by a combination of the methods used earlier in this chapter: graphing, substitution, and/or elimination.

Example **Find the coordinates of the vertices of the figure formed by** $5x + 4y < 20$, $y < 2x + 3$, **and** $x - 3y < 4$.

Graph the boundary of each inequality. The intersections of the boundary lines are the vertices of a triangle.

The vertex $(4, 0)$ can be determined from the graph. To find the coordinates of the second and third vertices, solve the two systems of equations

$$\begin{array}{l} y = 2x + 3 \\ 5x + 4y = 20 \end{array} \quad \text{and} \quad \begin{array}{l} y = 2x + 3 \\ x - 3y = 4 \end{array}$$

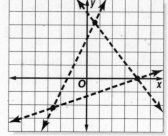

For the first system of equations, rewrite the first equation in standard form as $2x - y = -3$. Then multiply that equation by 4 and add to the second equation.

$$\begin{array}{l} 2x - y = -3 \quad \text{Multiply by 4.} \\ 5x + 4y = 20 \end{array} \qquad \begin{array}{r} 8x - 4y = -12 \\ (+) \ 5x + 4y = \ \ 20 \\ \hline 13x \ \ \ \ = \ \ \ 8 \\ x \ \ \ \ = \ \dfrac{8}{13} \end{array}$$

Then substitute $x = \dfrac{8}{13}$ in one of the original equations and solve for y.

$$2\left(\dfrac{8}{13}\right) - y = -3$$

$$\dfrac{16}{13} - y = -3$$

$$y = \dfrac{55}{13}$$

The coordinates of the second vertex are $\left(\dfrac{8}{13}, 4\dfrac{3}{13}\right)$.

For the second system of equations, use substitution.

Substitute $2x + 3$ for y in the second equation to get

$$x - 3(2x + 3) = 4$$
$$x - 6x - 9 = 4$$
$$-5x = 13$$
$$x = -\dfrac{13}{5}$$

Then substitute $x = -\dfrac{13}{5}$ in the first equation to solve for y.

$$y = 2\left(-\dfrac{13}{5}\right) + 3$$

$$y = -\dfrac{26}{5} + 3$$

$$y = -\dfrac{11}{5}$$

The coordinates of the third vertex are $\left(-2\dfrac{3}{5}, -2\dfrac{1}{5}\right)$.

Thus, the coordinates of the three vertices are $(4, 0)$, $\left(\dfrac{8}{13}, 4\dfrac{3}{13}\right)$, and $\left(-2\dfrac{3}{5}, -2\dfrac{1}{5}\right)$.

Exercises

Find the coordinates of the vertices of the figure formed by each system of inequalities.

1. $y \le -3x + 7$

$y < \dfrac{1}{2}x$

$y > -2$

2. $x > -3$

$y < -\dfrac{1}{3}x + 3$

$y > x - 1$

3. $y < -\dfrac{1}{2}x + 3$

$y > \dfrac{1}{2}x + 1$

$y < 3x + 10$

3-3 Skills Practice

Solving Systems of Inequalities by Graphing

Solve each system of inequalities by graphing.

1. $x < 1$
$y \geq -1$

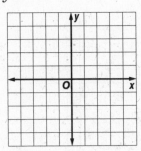

2. $x \geq -3$
$y \geq -3$

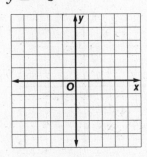

3. $x \leq 2$
$x > 4$

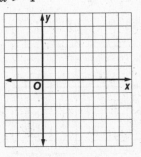

4. $y \geq x$
$y \geq -x$

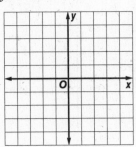

5. $y < -4x$
$y \geq 3x - 2$

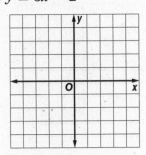

6. $x - y \geq -1$
$3x - y \leq 4$

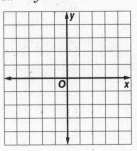

7. $y < 3$
$x + 2y < 12$

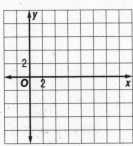

8. $y < -2x + 3$
$y \leq x - 2$

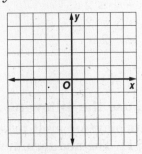

9. $x - y \leq 4$
$2x + y < 4$

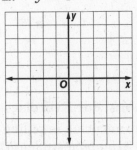

Find the coordinates of the vertices of the figure formed by each system of inequalities.

10. $y < 0$
$x < 0$
$y \geq -x - 1$

11. $y < 3 - x$
$y \geq 3$
$x > -5$

12. $x \geq -2$
$y > x - 2$
$x + y \leq 2$

Lesson 3-3

3-3 Practice

Solving Systems of Inequalities by Graphing

Solve each system of inequalities by graphing.

1. $y + 1 < -x$
$y \geq 1$

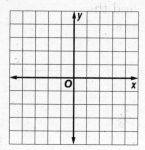

2. $x > -2$
$2y \geq 3x + 6$

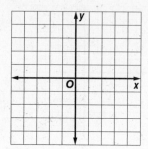

3. $y \leq 2x - 3$
$y \leq -\dfrac{1}{2}x + 2$

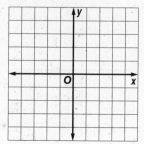

4. $x + y > -2$
$3x - y \geq -2$

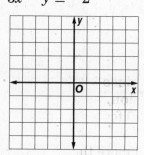

5. $|y| \leq 1$
$y < x - 1$

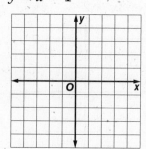

6. $3y > 4x$
$2x - 3y > -6$

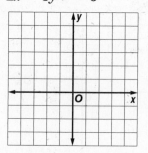

Find the coordinates of the vertices of the figure formed by each system of inequalities.

7. $y \geq 1 - x$
$y \leq x - 1$
$x \leq 3$

8. $x - y \leq 2$
$x + y \leq 2$
$x \geq -2$

9. $y \geq 2x - 2$
$2x + 3y \geq 6$
$y < 4$

DRAMA For Exercises 10 and 11, use the following information.

The drama club is selling tickets to its play. An adult ticket costs \$15 and a student ticket costs \$11. The auditorium will seat 300 ticket-holders. The drama club wants to collect at least \$3630 from ticket sales.

10. Write and graph a system of four inequalities that describe how many of each type of ticket the club must sell to meets its goal.

11. List three different combinations of tickets sold that satisfy the inequalities.

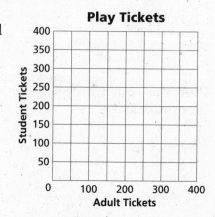

3-3 Word Problem Practice

Solving Systems of Inequalities by Graphing

1. BIRD BATH Melissa wants to put a bird bath in her yard at point (x, y), and wants it to be is inside the enclosed shaded area shown in the graph.

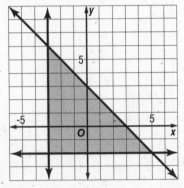

First, she checks that $x \geq -3$ and $y \geq -2$. What linear inequality must she check to conclude that (x, y) is inside the triangle?

2. SQUARES Matt finds a blot of ink covering his writing in his notes for math class. He sees "A square is defined by $|x| \leq 8$ and _". Write an inequality that completes this sentence.

3. HOLIDAY Amanda received presents and cards from friends over the holiday season. Every present came with one card and none of her friends sent her more than one card. Less than 10 of her friends sent only a card. Describe this situation using inequalities.

4. DECK The Wrights are building a deck. The deck is defined by the inequalities $x \leq 5$, $0.25x + y \geq -4.75$, $y \leq 5$, and $4.5x + y \geq -17.5$. Graph the inequalities and find the coordinates of the deck's corners.

TICKETS For Exercises 5 and 6, use the following information.
A theater charges $10 for adults and $5 for children 12 or under. The theater makes a profit if they can sell more than $600 worth of tickets. The theater has seating for 100 people.

5. Write a system of linear inequalities that describes the situation.

6. Graph the solution to the inequalities. Can the theater make a profit if no adults come to the performance?

Lesson 3-3

3-3   Enrichment

Creative Designs

A system of linear inequalities can be used to define the region bounded by a geometric shape graphed on a coordinate plane. For example, the rectangle shown can be defined by the system

$x \leq 4$
$x \geq 0$
$y \leq 3$
$y \geq 0.$

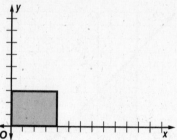

The triangle shown can be described using the inequalities

$x + 2y \leq 4$
$x \geq 0$
$y \geq 1.$

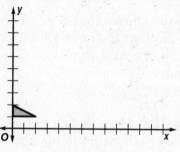

1. Find a system of linear inequalities to describe the area bounded by the bow tie shape below. The intersection points are (1, 1), (1, 4), (3, 3), (5, 2), and (5, 5).

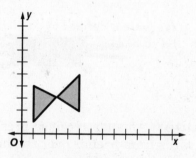

2. Find a system of linear inequalities to describe the area bounded by the basic 'house' shape shown below. The intersection points are (1,1), (1,5), (3,7), (5,5), and (5,1).

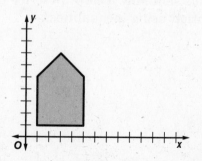

3-4 Lesson Reading Guide
Linear Programming

Get Ready for the Lesson

Read the introduction to Lesson 3-4 in your textbook.

Name two or more facts that indicate that you will need to use inequalities to model this situation.

Read the Lesson

1. Complete each sentence.

   a. When you find the feasible region for a linear programming problem, you are solving

      a system of linear _____ called _____. The points

      in the feasible region are _____ of the system.

   b. The corner points of a polygonal region are the _____ of the
      feasible region.

2. A polygonal region always takes up only a limited part of the coordinate plane. One way
   to think of this is to imagine a circle or rectangle that the region would fit inside. In the
   case of a polygonal region, you can always find a circle or rectangle that is large enough
   to contain all the points of the polygonal region. What word is used to describe a region
   that can be enclosed in this way? What word is used to describe a region that is too large
   to be enclosed in this way?

3. How do you find the corner points of the polygonal region in a linear programming
   problem?

4. What are some everyday meanings of the word *feasible* that remind you of the
   mathematical meaning of the term *feasible region*?

Remember What You Learned

5. Look up the word *constraint* in a dictionary. If more than one definition is given, choose
   the one that seems closest to the idea of a *constraint* in a linear programming problem.
   How can this definition help you to remember the meaning of *constraint* as it is used in
   this lesson?

Lesson 3-3

3-4 Study Guide and Intervention

Linear Programming

Maximum and Minimum Values When a system of linear inequalities produces a bounded polygonal region, the *maximum* or *minimum* value of a related function will occur at a vertex of the region.

Example Graph the system of inequalities. Name the coordinates of the vertices of the feasible region. Find the maximum and minimum values of the function $f(x, y) = 3x + 2y$ for this polygonal region.

$$y \le 4$$
$$y \le -x + 6$$
$$y \ge \frac{1}{2}x - \frac{3}{2}$$
$$y \le 6x + 4$$

First find the vertices of the bounded region. Graph the inequalities.

The polygon formed is a quadrilateral with vertices at $(0, 4)$, $(2, 4)$, $(5, 1)$, and $(-1, -2)$. Use the table to find the maximum and minimum values of $f(x, y) = 3x + 2y$.

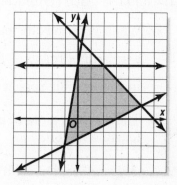

(x, y)	$3x + 2y$	$f(x, y)$
$(0, 4)$	$3(0) + 2(4)$	8
$(2, 4)$	$3(2) + 2(4)$	14
$(5, 1)$	$3(5) + 2(1)$	17
$(-1, -2)$	$3(-1) + 2(-2)$	-7

The maximum value is 17 at $(5, 1)$. The minimum value is -7 at $(-1, -2)$.

Exercises

Graph each system of inequalities. Name the coordinates of the vertices of the feasible region. Find the maximum and minimum values of the given function for this region.

1. $y \ge 2$
$1 \le x \le 5$
$y \le x + 3$
$f(x, y) = 3x - 2y$

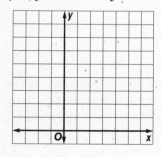

2. $y \ge -2$
$y \ge 2x - 4$
$x - 2y \ge -1$
$f(x, y) = 4x - y$

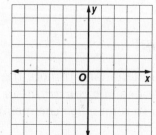

3. $x + y \ge 2$
$4y \le x + 8$
$y \ge 2x - 5$
$f(x, y) = 4x + 3y$

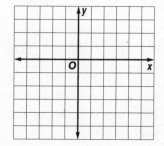

3-4 **Study Guide and Intervention** (continued)

Linear Programming

Real-World Problems When solving **linear programming** problems, use the following procedure.

1. Define variables.
2. Write a system of inequalities.
3. Graph the system of inequalities.
4. Find the coordinates of the vertices of the feasible region.
5. Write an expression to be maximized or minimized.
6. Substitute the coordinates of the vertices in the expression.
7. Select the greatest or least result to answer the problem.

Example A painter has exactly 32 units of yellow dye and 54 units of green dye. He plans to mix as many gallons as possible of color A and color B. Each gallon of color A requires 4 units of yellow dye and 1 unit of green dye. Each gallon of color B requires 1 unit of yellow dye and 6 units of green dye. Find the maximum number of gallons he can mix.

Step 1 Define the variables.

x = the number of gallons of color A made

y = the number of gallons of color B made

Step 2 Write a system of inequalities.

Since the number of gallons made cannot be negative, $x \geq 0$ and $y \geq 0$.

There are 32 units of yellow dye; each gallon of color A requires 4 units, and each gallon of color B requires 1 unit.

So $4x + y \leq 32$.

Similarly for the green dye, $x + 6y \leq 54$.

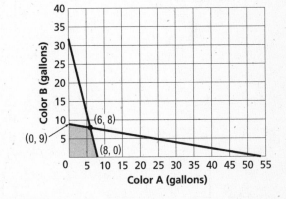

Steps 3 and 4 Graph the system of inequalities and find the coordinates of the vertices of the feasible region. The vertices of the feasible region are (0, 0), (0, 9), (6, 8), and (8, 0).

Steps 5–7 Find the maximum number of gallons, $x + y$, that he can make. The maximum number of gallons the painter can make is 14, 6 gallons of color A and 8 gallons of color B.

Exercises

1. **FOOD** A delicatessen has 12 pounds of plain sausage and 10 pounds of spicy sausage. A pound of Bratwurst A contains $\frac{3}{4}$ pound of plain sausage and $\frac{1}{4}$ pound of spicy sausage. A pound of Bratwurst B contains $\frac{1}{2}$ pound of each sausage.

   Find the maximum number of pounds of bratwurst that can be made.

2. **MANUFACTURING** Machine A can produce 30 steering wheels per hour at a cost of $8 per hour. Machine B can produce 40 steering wheels per hour at a cost of $12 per hour. The company can use either machine by itself or both machines at the same time. What is the minimum number of hours needed to produce 380 steering wheels if the cost must be no more than $108?

Lesson 3-4

3-4 Skills Practice

Linear Programming

Graph each system of inequalities. Name the coordinates of the vertices of the feasible region. Find the maximum and minimum values of the given function for this region.

1. $x \geq 2$
$x \leq 5$
$y \geq 1$
$y \leq 4$
$f(x, y) = x + y$

2. $x \geq 1$
$y \leq 6$
$y \geq x - 2$
$f(x, y) = x - y$

3. $x \geq 0$
$y \geq 0$
$y \leq 7 - x$
$f(x, y) = 3x + y$

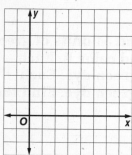
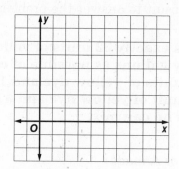
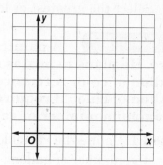

4. $x \geq -1$
$x + y \leq 6$
$f(x, y) = x + 2y$

5. $y \leq 2x$
$y \geq 6 - x$
$y \leq 6$
$f(x, y) = 4x + 3y$

6. $y \geq -x - 2$
$y \geq 3x + 2$
$y \leq x + 4$
$f(x, y) = -3x + 5y$

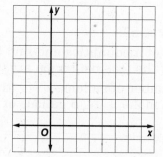
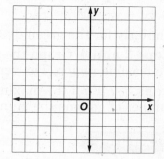

7. MANUFACTURING A backpack manufacturer produces an internal frame pack and an external frame pack. Let x represent the number of internal frame packs produced in one hour and let y represent the number of external frame packs produced in one hour. Then the inequalities $x + 3y \leq 18$, $2x + y \leq 16$, $x \geq 0$, and $y \geq 0$ describe the constraints for manufacturing both packs. Use the profit function $f(x) = 50x + 80y$ and the constraints given to determine the maximum profit for manufacturing both backpacks for the given constraints.

30

3-4 Practice

Linear Programming

Graph each system of inequalities. Name the coordinates of the vertices of the feasible region. Find the maximum and minimum values of the given function for this region.

1. $2x - 4 \leq y$
$-2x - 4 \leq y$
$y \leq 2$
$f(x, y) = -2x + y$

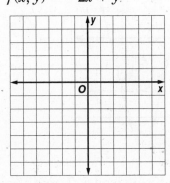

2. $3x - y \leq 7$
$2x - y \geq 3$
$y \geq x - 3$
$f(x, y) = x - 4y$

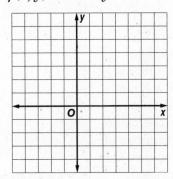

3. $x \geq 0$
$y \geq 0$
$y \leq 6$
$y \leq -3x + 15$
$f(x, y) = 3x + y$

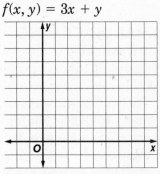

4. $x \leq 0$
$y \leq 0$
$4x + y \geq -7$
$f(x, y) = -x - 4y$

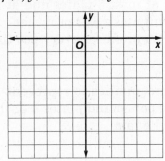

5. $y \leq 3x + 6$
$4y + 3x \leq 3$
$x \geq -2$
$f(x, y) = -x + 3y$

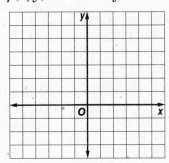

6. $2x + 3y \geq 6$
$2x - y \leq 2$
$x \geq 0$
$y \geq 0$
$f(x, y) = x + 4y + 3$

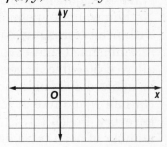

PRODUCTION For Exercises 7–9, use the following information.

A glass blower can form 8 simple vases or 2 elaborate vases in an hour. In a work shift of no more than 8 hours, the worker must form at least 40 vases.

7. Let s represent the hours forming simple vases and e the hours forming elaborate vases. Write a system of inequalities involving the time spent on each type of vase.

8. If the glass blower makes a profit of $30 per hour worked on the simple vases and $35 per hour worked on the elaborate vases, write a function for the total profit on the vases.

9. Find the number of hours the worker should spend on each type of vase to maximize profit. What is that profit?

31

Lesson 3-4

3-4 **Word Problem Practice**

Linear Programming

1. REGIONS A region in the plane is formed by the equations $x - y < 3$, $x - y > -3$, and $x + y > -3$. Is this region bounded or unbounded? Explain.

2. MANUFACTURING Eighty workers are available to assemble tables and chairs. It takes 5 people to assemble a table and 3 people to assemble a chair. The workers always make at least as many tables as chairs because the tables are easier to make. If x is the number of tables and y is the number of chairs, the system of inequalities that represent what can be assembled is $x > 0$, $y > 0$, $y \le x$, and $5x + 3y \le 80$. What is the maximum total number of chairs and tables the workers can make?

3. FISH An aquarium is 2000 cubic inches. Nathan wants to populate the aquarium with neon tetras and catfish. It is recommended that each neon tetra be allowed 50 cubic inches and each catfish be allowed 200 cubic inches of space. Nathan would like at least one catfish for every 4 neon tetras. Let n be the number of neon tetra and c be the number of catfish. The following inequalities form the feasible region for this situation: $n > 0$, $c > 0$, $4c \ge n$, and $50n + 200c \le 2000$. What is the maximum number of fish Nathan can put in his aquarium?

4. ELEVATION A trapezoidal park is built on a slight incline. The function for the ground elevation above sea level is $f(x, y) = x - 3y + 20$ feet. What are the coordinates of the highest point in the park?

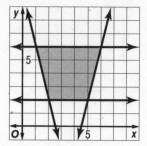

CERAMICS For Exercises 5–7, use the following information.
Josh has 8 days to make pots and plates to sell at a local fair. Each pot weighs 2 pounds and each plate weighs 1 pound. Josh cannot carry more than 50 pounds to the fair. Each day, he can make at most 5 plates and at most 3 pots. He will make $12 profit for every plate and $25 profit for every pot that he sells.

5. Write linear inequalities to represent the number of pots p and plates a Josh may bring to the fair.

6. List the coordinates of the vertices of the feasible region.

7. How many pots and how many plates should Josh make to maximize his potential profit?

3-4 Enrichment

Sensitivity Analysis

A linear programming model has specific objective coefficients. For example, if the value of a model is found by $2x + 3y = 5$, the objective coefficients are {2, 3}. What if these coefficients were {2.1, 2.9} or {2.5, 3.1}? How would these changes affect the optimal linear program value? This type of investigation is called **sensitivity analysis**.

In general, the objective function in two-variable linear programming problem can be written as: maximize (or minimize) $Ax + By = C$, subject to a set of constraint equations. Changes to the *parameters* A and B could change the slope of the line. This change of slope could lead to a change in the optimum solution to a different corner point (Recall, the optimum solution occurs at a *corner point*).

There is a range in the slope value that will produce this change, thus there is a range of variation for both A and B that will keep the optimal solution the same (see graph).

1. Find the slope of $Ax + By = C$ and observe how changes to the parameters A and B can change the slope of the line.

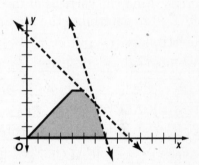

Consider the Linear Programming problem:

Maximize: $C = 2x + 3y$,
Subject to: $3x + y \leq 21$
$x + y \leq 9$
$y \leq x$
$y \leq 4$

(x, y)	$(0, 0)$	$(4, 4)$	$(5, 4)$	$(6, 3)$	$(7, 0)$
C	0	20	22	21	14

After finding the intersections and evaluating the objective equation, we find the maximal solution is (5, 4). If the objective coefficients are changed from 2 and 3 to A and B, the optimum solution with remain at (5, 4) while the slope remains between the slope of $x + y \leq 9$ and the slope of $3x + y \leq 21$. If not, then the new optimal solution will be at (4, 4) or (6, 3).

2. Express the relationship, the slope of the objective function is between the slope of the line $x + y = 9$ and the slope of the line $3x + y = 21$, algebraically.

3. Determine the range on A if B remains equal to 3.

Lesson 3-4

3-4 Graphing Calculator Activity

Linear Programming

A graphing calculator can store the x- and y-coordinates when using the **intersect** command in the [CALC] menu. This can be displayed on the home screen and used to evaluate an expression with x and y variables. This process is useful in finding the vertices of the feasible region and determining the maximum or minimum value for $f(x, y)$.

Example   Graph the system $x - 3y \geq -7$, $5x + y \leq 13$, $x + 6y \geq -9$, $3x - 2y \geq -7$, and $f(x, y) = 4x - 3y$. **Find the coordinates of the feasible region. Then find the maximum and minimum values for the system.**

Solve each inequality for y. Enter each boundary equation in the **Y=** screen. Find the vertices of the feasible region. Then find the values of $f(x, y)$ to determine the maximum and minimum values.

Keystrokes: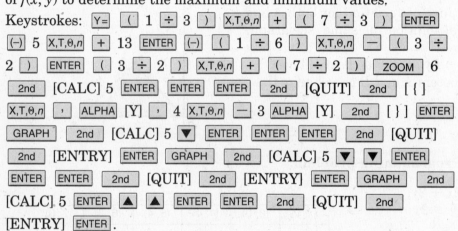

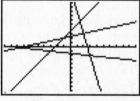

[−10, 10] scl:1 by [−10, 10] scl:1

The maximum value of the system is 18 and the minimum value is −10.

Exercises

Graph each system. Find the coordinates of the vertices of the feasible region. Then find the maximum and minimum values for the system.

1. $2x + 3y \geq 6$
   $3x - 2y \geq -4$
   $5x + y \geq 15$
   $f(x, y) = x + 3y$

2. $y \leq 4x + 6$
   $x + 4y \leq 7$
   $2x + y \leq 7$
   $x - 6y \leq 10$
   $f(x, y) = 2x - y$

3. $y \leq 16 - x$
   $0 \leq 2y \leq 17$
   $2x + 3y \geq 11$
   $y \leq 3x + 1$
   $y \geq 2x - 13$
   $y \geq 7 - 2x$
   $f(x, y) = 5x + 6y$

3-5 Lesson Reading Guide

Solving Systems of Equations in Three Variables

Get Ready for the Lesson

Read the introduction to Lesson 3-5 in your textbook.

At the 1960 Summer Olympics in Rome, Italy, the United States won 71 medals. The U.S. team won 13 more gold medals than silver and 5 fewer bronze medals than silver. Using the same variables as those in the introduction, write a system of equations that describes the medals won for the 1960 Olympics.

Read the Lesson

1. The planes for the equations in a system of three linear equations in three variables determine the number of solutions. Match each graph description below with the description of the number of solutions of the system. (Some of the items on the right may be used more than once, and not all possible types of graphs are listed.)

   a. three parallel planes _____

   b. three planes that intersect in a line _____

   c. three planes that intersect in one point _____

   d. one plane that represents all three equations _____

   I.   one solution

   II. no solutions

   III. infinite solutions

2. Suppose that three classmates, Monique, Josh, and Lilly, are studying for a quiz on this lesson. They work together on solving a system of equations in three variables, $x, y,$ and z, following the algebraic method shown in your textbook. They first find that $z = 3$, then that $y = -2$, and finally that $x = -1$. The students agree on these values, but disagree on how to write the solution. Here are their answers:

   Monique: $(3, -2, -1)$ Josh: $(-2, -1, 3)$ Lilly: $(-1, -2, 3)$

   a. How do you think each student decided on the order of the numbers in the ordered triple?

   b. Which student is correct?

Remember What You Learned

3. How can you remember that obtaining the equation $0 = 0$ indicates a system with infinitely many solutions, while obtaining an equation such as $0 = 8$ indicates a system with no solutions?

Lesson 3-4

3-5 Study Guide and Intervention

Solving Systems of Equations in Three Variables

Systems in Three Variables Use the methods used for solving systems of linear equations in two variables to solve systems of equations in three variables. A system of three equations in three variables can have a unique solution, infinitely many solutions, or no solution. A solution is an **ordered triple**.

Example Solve this system of equations.

$$3x + y - z = -6$$
$$2x - y + 2z = 8$$
$$4x + y - 3z = -21$$

Step 1 Use elimination to make a system of two equations in two variables.

$3x + y - z = -6$	First equation	$2x - y + 2z = 8$	Second equation
$(+) 2x - y + 2z = 8$	Second equation	$(+) 4x + y - 3z = -21$	Third equation
$5x + z = 2$	Add to eliminate y.	$6x - z = -13$	Add to eliminate y.

Step 2 Solve the system of two equations.

$$5x + z = 2$$
$$(+) 6x - z = -13$$

$11x = -11$ Add to eliminate z.

$x = -1$ Divide both sides by 11.

Substitute -1 for x in one of the equations with two variables and solve for z.

$5x + z = 2$ Equation with two variables

$5(-1) + z = 2$ Replace x with -1.

$-5 + z = 2$ Multiply.

$z = 7$ Add 5 to both sides.

The result so far is $x = -1$ and $z = 7$.

Step 3 Substitute -1 for x and 7 for z in one of the original equations with three variables.

$3x + y - z = -6$ Original equation with three variables

$3(-1) + y - 7 = -6$ Replace x with -1 and z with 7.

$-3 + y - 7 = -6$ Multiply.

$y = 4$ Simplify.

The solution is $(-1, 4, 7)$.

Exercises

Solve each system of equations.

1. $2x + 3y - z = 0$
$x - 2y - 4z = 14$
$3x + y - 8z = 17$

2. $2x - y + 4z = 11$
$x + 2y - 6z = -11$
$3x - 2y - 10z = 11$

3. $x - 2y + z = 8$
$2x + y - z = 0$
$3x - 6y + 3z = 24$

4. $3x - y - z = 5$
$3x + 2y - z = 11$
$6x - 3y + 2z = -12$

5. $2x - 4y - z = 10$
$4x - 8y - 2z = 16$
$3x + y + z = 12$

6. $x - 6y + 4z = 2$
$2x + 4y - 8z = 16$
$x - 2y = 5$

3-5 **Study Guide and Intervention** *(continued)*

Solving Systems of Equations in Three Variables

Real-World Problems

Example The Laredo Sports Shop sold 10 balls, 3 bats, and 2 bases for $99 on Monday. On Tuesday they sold 4 balls, 8 bats, and 2 bases for $78. On Wednesday they sold 2 balls, 3 bats, and 1 base for $33.60. What are the prices of 1 ball, 1 bat, and 1 base?

First define the variables.
x = price of 1 ball
y = price of 1 bat
z = price of 1 base

Translate the information in the problem into three equations.

$10x + 3y + 2z = 99$
$4x + 8y + 2z = 78$
$2x + 3y + z = 33.60$

Subtract the second equation from the first equation to eliminate z.

$$\begin{array}{r} 10x + 3y + 2z = 99 \\ (-)\ \ 4x + 8y + 2z = 78 \\ \hline 6x - 5y\ \ \ \ \ \ \ = 21 \end{array}$$

Multiply the third equation by 2 and subtract from the second equation.

$$\begin{array}{r} 4x + 8y + 2z = 78 \\ (-)\ 4x + 6y + 2z = 67.20 \\ \hline 2y\ \ \ \ \ \ \ = 10.80 \\ y\ \ \ \ \ = 5.40 \end{array}$$

Substitute 5.40 for y in the equation $6x - 5y = 21$.

$6x - 5(5.40) = 21$
$6x = 48$
$x = 8$

Substitute 8 for x and 5.40 for y in one of the original equations to solve for z.

$10x + 3y + 2z = 99$
$10(8) + 3(5.40) + 2z = 99$
$80 + 16.20 + 2z = 99$
$2z = 2.80$
$z = 1.40$

So a ball costs $8, a bat $5.40, and a base $1.40.

Exercises

1. **FITNESS TRAINING** Carly is training for a triathlon. In her training routine each week, she runs 7 times as far as she swims, and she bikes 3 times as far as she runs. One week she trained a total of 232 miles. How far did she run that week?

2. **ENTERTAINMENT** At the arcade, Ryan, Sara, and Tim played video racing games, pinball, and air hockey. Ryan spent $6 for 6 racing games, 2 pinball games, and 1 game of air hockey. Sara spent $12 for 3 racing games, 4 pinball games, and 5 games of air hockey. Tim spent $12.25 for 2 racing games, 7 pinball games, and 4 games of air hockey. How much did each of the games cost?

3. **FOOD** A natural food store makes its own brand of trail mix out of dried apples, raisins, and peanuts. One pound of the mixture costs $3.18. It contains twice as much peanuts by weight as apples. One pound of dried apples costs $4.48, a pound of raisins $2.40, and a pound of peanuts $3.44. How many ounces of each ingredient are contained in 1 pound of the trail mix?

Lesson 3-5

3-5 **Skills Practice**

Solving Systems of Equations in Three Variables

Solve each system of equations.

1. $2a + c = -10$
$b - c = 15$
$a - 2b + c = -5$

2. $x + y + z = 3$
$13x + 2z = 2$
$-x - 5z = -5$

3. $2x + 5y + 2z = 6$
$5x - 7y = -29$
$z = 1$

4. $x + 4y - z = 1$
$3x - y + 8z = 0$
$x + 4y - z = 10$

5. $-2z = -6$
$2x + 3y - z = -2$
$x + 2y + 3z = 9$

6. $3x - 2y + 2z = -2$
$x + 6y - 2z = -2$
$x + 2y = 0$

7. $-x - 5z = -5$
$y - 3x = 0$
$13x + 2z = 2$

8. $-3r + 2t = 1$
$4r + s - 2t = -6$
$r + s + 4t = 3$

9. $x - y + 3z = 3$
$-2x + 2y - 6z = 6$
$y - 5z = -3$

10. $5m + 3n + p = 4$
$3m + 2n = 0$
$2m - n + 3p = 8$

11. $2x + 2y + 2z = -2$
$2x + 3y + 2z = 4$
$x + y + z = -1$

12. $x + 2y - z = 4$
$3x - y + 2z = 3$
$-x + 3y + z = 6$

13. $3x - 2y + z = 1$
$-x + y - z = 2$
$5x + 2y + 10z = 39$

14. $3x - 5y + 2z = -12$
$x + 4y - 2z = 8$
$-3x + 5y - 2z = 12$

15. $2x + y + 3z = -2$
$x - y - z = -3$
$3x - 2y + 3z = -12$

16. $2x - 4y + 3z = 0$
$x - 2y - 5z = 13$
$5x + 3y - 2z = 19$

17. $-2x + y + 2z = 2$
$3x + 3y + z = 0$
$x + y + z = 2$

18. $x - 2y + 2z = -1$
$x + 2y - z = 6$
$-3x + 6y - 6z = 3$

19. The sum of three numbers is 18. The sum of the first and second numbers is 15, and the first number is 3 times the third number. Find the numbers.

3-5 Practice

Solving Systems of Equations in Three Variables

Solve each system of equations.

1. $2x - y + 2z = 15$
$-x + y + z = 3$
$3x - y + 2z = 18$

2. $x - 4y + 3z = -27$
$2x + 2y - 3z = 22$
$4z = -16$

3. $a + b = 3$
$-b + c = 3$
$a + 2c = 10$

4. $3m - 2n + 4p = 15$
$m - n + p = 3$
$m + 4n - 5p = 0$

5. $2g + 3h - 8j = 10$
$g - 4h = 1$
$-2g - 3h + 8j = 5$

6. $2x + y - z = -8$
$4x - y + 2z = -3$
$-3x + y + 2z = 5$

7. $2x - 5y + z = 5$
$3x + 2y - z = 17$
$4x - 3y + 2z = 17$

8. $2x + 3y + 4z = 2$
$5x - 2y + 3z = 0$
$x - 5y - 2z = -4$

9. $p + 4r = -7$
$p - 3q = -8$
$q + r = 1$

10. $4x + 4y - 2z = 8$
$3x - 5y + 3z = 0$
$2x + 2y - z = 4$

11. $d + 3e + f = 0$
$-d + 2e + f = -1$
$4d + e - f = 1$

12. $4x + y + 5z = -9$
$x - 4y - 2z = -2$
$2x + 3y - 2z = 21$

13. $5x + 9y + z = 20$
$2x - y - z = -21$
$5x + 2y + 2z = -21$

14. $2x + y - 3z = -3$
$3x + 2y + 4z = 5$
$-6x - 3y + 9z = 9$

15. $3x + 3y + z = 10$
$5x + 2y + 2z = 7$
$3x - 2y + 3z = -9$

16. $2u + v + w = 2$
$-3u + 2v + 3w = 7$
$-u - v + 2w = 7$

17. $x + 5y - 3z = -18$
$3x - 2y + 5z = 22$
$-2x - 3y + 8z = 28$

18. $x - 2y + z = -1$
$-x + 2y - z = 6$
$-4y + 2z = 1$

19. $2x - 2y - 4z = -2$
$3x - 3y - 6z = -3$
$-2x + 3y + z = 7$

20. $x - y + 9z = -27$
$2x - 4y - z = -1$
$3x + 6y - 3z = 27$

21. $2x - 5y - 3z = 7$
$-4x + 10y + 2z = 6$
$6x - 15y - z = -19$

22. The sum of three numbers is 6. The third number is the sum of the first and second numbers. The first number is one more than the third number. Find the numbers.

23. The sum of three numbers is -4. The second number decreased by the third is equal to the first. The sum of the first and second numbers is -5. Find the numbers.

24. **SPORTS** Alexandria High School scored 37 points in a football game. Six points are awarded for each touchdown. After each touchdown, the team can earn one point for the extra kick or two points for a 2-point conversion. The team scored one fewer 2-point conversions than extra kicks. The team scored 10 times during the game. How many touchdowns were made during the game?

39

3-5 Word Problem Practice

Solving Systems of Equations in Three Variables

1. SIBLINGS Amy, Karen, and Nolan are siblings. Their ages in years can be represented by the variables A, K, and N, respectively. They have lived a total of 22 years combined. Karen has lived twice as many years as Amy, and Nolan has lived 6 years longer than Amy. Use the equations $A + K + N = 22$, $K = 2A$, and $N = A + 6$ to find the age of each sibling.

2. HOCKEY Bobby Hull scored G goals, A assists, and P points in his NHL career. By definition, $P = G + A$. He scored 50 more goals than assists. Had he scored 15 more goals and 15 more assists, he would have scored 1200 points. How many goals, assists, and points did Bobby Hull score?

3. EXERCISE Larry, Camille, and Simone are keeping track of how far they walk each day. At the end of the week, they combined their distances and found that they had walked 34 miles in total. They also learned that Camille walked twice as far as Larry, and that Larry walked 2 more miles than Simone. How far did each person walk?

DISTANCES For Exercises 4 and 5, use the following information.
Let c be the distance between Carlisle and Wellesley, let b be the distance between Carlisle and Stonebridge, and let a be the distance between Wellesley and Stonebridge.

- If you did a circuit, traveling from Carlisle to Wellesley to Stonebridge and back to Carlisle, you would travel 73 miles.
- Stonebridge is 12 miles farther than Wellesley is from Carlisle.
- If you drove from Stonebridge to Carlisle and back to Stonebridge, and then continued to Wellesley then back to Stonebridge, you would travel 102 miles.

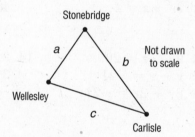

4. Write a system of linear equations to represent the situation.

5. Solve the system of equations. Explain the meaning of the solution in the context of the situation.

3-5 Enrichment

Homogenous Systems

A system of equations is called homogeneous if it is of the form:

$$gz + hy + kz = 0$$
$$dx + ey + fz = 0$$
$$ax + by + cz = 0$$

Homogeneous systems have some unique characteristics that set them apart from general systems of equations. The following exercises will explore some of these unique characteristics.

1. Evaluate the following statement. Is this statement *always*, *sometimes*, or *never* true? Expalin your reasoning.
   Every homogeneous system of equations will have at least one trivial solution: (0, 0, 0).

2. Find a non-trivial solution to the following homogenous system of equations.
   $$x + y + 5z = 0$$
   $$2x + y + 7z = 0$$
   $$x + 2z = 0$$

3. Multiply the solution you found in Exercise 2 by 3. Is the new ordered triple a solution to the system?

4. Multiply the solution you found in Exercise 2 by -6. Is the new ordered triple a solution to the system?

5. Make a conjecture about any multiple of a given solution to a homogeneous system of equations.

6. Make a conjecture about the number of solutions that a homogeneous system of equations will have if it has at least one non-trivial solution.

3 Student Recording Sheet

1. Ⓐ Ⓑ Ⓒ Ⓓ

2. Ⓕ Ⓖ Ⓗ Ⓙ

3. Record your answer and fill in the bubbles in the grid below. Be sure to use the correct place value.

4. Ⓐ Ⓑ Ⓒ Ⓓ

5. Ⓕ Ⓖ Ⓗ Ⓙ

6. Ⓐ Ⓑ Ⓒ Ⓓ

7. Ⓕ Ⓖ Ⓗ Ⓙ

8. Ⓐ Ⓑ Ⓒ Ⓓ

9. Ⓕ Ⓖ Ⓗ Ⓙ

10. Record your answer and fill in the bubbles in the grid below. Be sure to use the correct place value.

Pre-AP

Record your answers for Question 11 on the back of this paper.

Assessment

3 Rubric for Scoring Pre-AP

General Scoring Guidelines

- If a student gives only a correct numerical answer to a problem but does not show how he or she arrived at the answer, the student will be awarded only 1 credit. All extended response questions require the student to show work.

- A fully correct answer for a multiple-part question requires correct responses for all parts of the question. For example, if a question has three parts, the correct response to one or two parts of the question that required work to be shown is *not* considered a fully correct response.

- Students who use trial and error to solve a problem must show their method. Merely showing that the answer checks or is correct is not considered a complete response for full credit.

Exercise 14 Rubric

Score	Specific Criteria
4	The equation and variables used to represent the total points scored are correct, $p = f + 2g + 3p$. The explanation shows that after 12 free throws and 2 three-point baskets were scored, 45 points had to be scored for two-point baskets. 45 is *not* evenly divisible by 2, therefore both Josh and Soledad cannot be correct.
3	The equation is written correctly. However, the explanation is correct but not complete. **OR** The explanation is correct and complete, but one error was made in writing the equation.
2	The equation is written correctly, but the explanation is incorrect or not given. **OR** The explanation is correct and complete, but the equation is incorrect or not given.
1	The explanation is incorrect or not given and only part of the equation is correct.
0	Response is completely incorrect.

3 Chapter 3 Quiz 1
(Lessons 3-1 and 3-2)

1. Solve the system $x + y = 4$ and $x - 2y = 1$ by graphing.

2. Graph the system $y = x + 2$ and $2y = 2x - 4$ and describe it as *consistent and independent*, *consistent and dependent*, or *inconsistent*.

3. Use substitution to solve the system of equations.

   $3y = 2x,$

   $y = \frac{2}{3}x - 2$

4. Use elimination to solve the system of equations.

   $4x - 5y = -2$

   $3x + 2y = -13$

5. **MULTIPLE CHOICE** Car Rentals rents cars and trucks for $25 and $30 a day, respectively. Last Tuesday, they rented all but 7 rental vehicles and reported $195 in lost rent. How many trucks were not rented last Tuesday?

   A. 3   **B.** 4   **C.** 5   **D.** 6

1.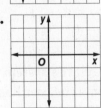

2.

3. _____

4. _____

5. _____

---

3 Chapter 3 Quiz 2
(Lesson 3-3)

Solve each system of inequalities by graphing.

1. $x - y > -3$

   $2x + y < 6$

2. $y \le \frac{1}{3}x + 1$

   $y > \frac{1}{3}x - 2$

Find the coordinates of the vertices of the figure formed by each system of inequalities.

3. $x \ge 0$

   $y \ge 0$

   $2x + y \le 4$

4. $y \ge -2$

   $x \le 3$

   $x + y \le 2$

   $y \le 2x - 4$

5. Tonya can earn $10 an hour painting houses and $15 an hour baby-sitting. She cannot work more than 15 hours per week. Write a system of inequalities that Tonya can use to determine how many hours a week she needs to work at painting x and baby-sitting y to earn $150 per week.

1.

2.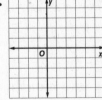

3. _____

4. _____

5. _____

3 **Chapter 3 Quiz 3**

SCORE _____

(Lesson 3-4)

1. A feasible region has vertices at $(-2, 3)$, $(1, 6)$, $(1, -1)$, and $(-3, -2)$. Find the maximum and minimum of the function $f(x, y) = -x + 2y$ over this region.

For questions 2–4, use the following system of inequalities.

$4y \leq x + 12$
$-4y \leq 3x + 4$
$5x - 4y \leq 4$
$f(x, y) = x - 5y$

2. Graph the system of inequalities.
3. Name the coordinates of the vertices of the feasible region.
4. Find the maximum and minimum values of the given function for this region.
5. A clothing company makes jackets and pants. Each jacket requires 1 hour of cutting and 4 hours of sewing. Each pair of pants requires 2 hours of cutting and 2 hours of sewing. The total time per day available for cutting is 20 hours and for sewing is 32 hours. Let j represent the number of jackets and let p represent the number of pairs of pants. Write a system of inequalities to represent the number of items that can be produced.

1. _____

2.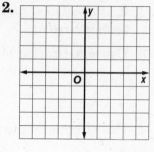

3. _____

4. _____

5. _____

---

3 **Chapter 3 Quiz 4**

SCORE _____

(Lesson 3-5)

Solve each system of equations.

1. $4x + 6y - 3z = 20$
   $x - 5y + z = -15$
   $-7x + y + 2z = 1$

2. $3x - y + 2z = 1$
   $-2x = -4$
   $x + 3y = 11$

3. $x + 2y - z = -7$
   $3x - 3y + z = 13$
   $2x + 5y + 2z = 0$

During one month, a rental car agency rented a total of 155 cars, vans, and trucks. Nine times as many cars were rented as vans, and three times as many vans were rented as trucks.

4. Let x represent the number of cars, let y represent the number of vans, and let z represent the number of trucks. Write a system of three equations that represents the number of vehicles rented.
5. Find the number of each type of vehicle rented.

1. _____

2. _____

3. _____

4. _____

5. _____

Assessment

1. Choose the correct description of the system of equations.
$3x - y = 5$
$6x = 2y + 5$

   A. consistent and independent   **C.** inconsistent
   B. consistent and dependent   **D.** inconsistent and dependent   1. _____

2. Solve $3x + 2y = 7$ and $x - 4y = -21$ by using substitution.

   F. $(3, -1)$ **G.** $\left(\dfrac{7}{3}, \dfrac{7}{2}\right)$ **H.** $(-1, 5)$ **J.** $(1, 5)$ 2. _____

Solve each system of equations by using elimination.

3. $2x + 5y = 18$ **A.** $(-1, 4)$ **C.** $(1, 4)$
   $3x - 2y = -11$ **B.** $\left(9, \dfrac{18}{5}\right)$ **D.** $(-3, 1)$ 3. _____

4. $3x - 5y = 14$ **F.** $(3, -1)$ **H.** $(8, 2)$
   $2x + 3y = 3$ **G.** $(0, 1)$ **J.** $(6, -3)$ 4. _____

Part II

5. Solve the system of equations by graphing.
$3x + y = -4$
$x - 2y = -6$

5.

6. The sides of an angle are parts of two lines whose equations are $2x - y = -1$ and $x + y = 4$. The angle's vertex is the point where the two parts meet. Graph the two lines and label the coordinates of the vertex of the angle.

6.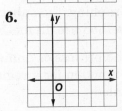

7. Classify the system as *consistent and independent, consistent and dependent*, or *inconsistent*.

   $3x - y = 5$
   $6x = 2(y + 5)$

7. _____

8. Solve the system of inequalities by graphing.

   $4x - y \geq 4$
   $3y < -x + 6$

8.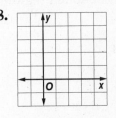

9. Find the coordinates of the vertices of the figure formed by the system of inequalities.

   $x \geq -2$
   $y \leq 6$
   $y \leq -\dfrac{3}{2}x + 6$
   $x + 2y \geq 4$

9. _____

3   Chapter 3 Vocabulary Test

bounded region	elimination method	linear programming	system of inequalities
consistent system	feasible region	ordered triple	unbounded region
constraints	inconsistent system	substitution method	vertex
dependent system	independent system	system of equations	

Choose from the terms above to complete each sentence.

1. A system of equations with no solutions is called a(n) _____.   1. _____

2. A(n) _____ is a system of equations with an infinite number of solutions.

   2. _____

3. $(3, -2, 7)$ is an example of a(n) _____.   3. _____

4. If your first step in solving a system of equations is to solve one of the equations for one variable in terms of the others, you are using the _____.

   4. _____

5. In a linear programming problem, the inequalities are called _____.

   5. _____

6. A set of two or more inequalities that are considered together is called a(n) _____.

   6. _____

7. If you are solving a system of equations and one of your steps is to add the equations, you are using the _____.

   7. _____

8. If you are solving a system of equations by graphing and your graph shows two intersecting lines, the system can be described both as a(n) _____ and as an independent system.   8. _____

9. Graphing, the substitution method, and the elimination method are all methods for solving a(n) _____.

   9. _____

10. The process of finding the maximum or minimum values of a function for a region defined by inequalities is called _____.

   10. _____

Define each term in your own words.

11. feasible region

12. unbounded region

Write the letter for the correct answer in the blank at the right of each question.

1. A system of equations may *not* have

   A. exactly one solution.

   B. no solution.

   C. infinitely many solutions.

   D. exactly two solutions.

   1. _____

Choose the correct description of each system of equations.

   F. consistent and independent

   G. inconsistent

   H. consistent and dependent

   J. inconsistent and dependent

   2. _____

2. $4x + 2y = -6$
   $2x + y = 8$

3. $3x + y = 3$
   $x - 2y = 4$

   3. _____

To solve each system of equations, which expression could be substituted for x into the first equation?

4. $5x - 2y = 8$
   $x - y = 1$

   A. $y + 1$

   B. $y - 1$

   C. $-\frac{2}{5}x + \frac{5}{8}$

   D. $x - 1$

   4. _____

5. $4x + 3y = 12$
   $x + 3y = -5$

   F. $3y - 5$

   G. $-3y - 5$

   H. $y + 35$

   J. $-\frac{1}{3}x - \frac{5}{3}$

   5. _____

The first equation of each system is multiplied by 4. By what number would you multiply the second equation in order to eliminate the x variable by adding?

6. $3x - 2y = 4$
   $4x + 5y = 28$

   A. 3

   B. -3

   C. 4

   D. -4

   6. _____

7. $-6x - 3y = 12$
   $8x + 2y = 16$

   F. 3

   G. 6

   H. -3

   J. -6

   7. _____

Solve each system of equations.

8. $3x - 2y = 5$
   $x = y + 2$

   A. $(1, 1)$

   B. $(2, 0)$

   C. $(0, -2)$

   D. $(1, -1)$

   8. _____

9. $2x + 3y = 5$
   $3x - 2y = 1$

   F. $(3, 4)$

   G. $(1, 1)$

   H. $(-2, 3)$

   J. $(4, -1)$

   9. _____

10. Which system of equations is graphed?

    A. $y - \frac{1}{3}x = 0$
    $x - y = -2$

    B. $y - 3x = 0$
    $x - y = -2$

    C. $y - 3x = 0$
    $x - y = 2$

    D. $y - \frac{1}{3}x = 0$
    $x - y = 2$

    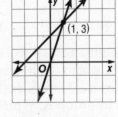

    10. _____

11. Which system of inequalities is graphed?

    F. $y > -1$
    $y \geq -x + 1$

    G. $y \geq -1$
    $y \geq -x + 1$

    H. $y > -1$
    $y \leq -x + 1$

    J. $y > -1$
    $y < -x + 1$

    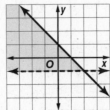

    11. _____

12. Find the coordinates of the vertices of the figure formed by the system $y \geq 0, x \geq 0, y \leq 2$, and $x \leq 3$.

   A. $(0, 0), (3, 0), (3, 2), (0, 2)$
   B. $(0, 0), (2, 0), (2, 3), (0, 3)$
   C. $(0, 0), (-3, 0), (-3, -2), (0, -2)$
   D. $(0, 0), (-2, 0), (-2, -3), (0, -3)$ 12. _____

Use the system of inequalities $y \geq 0$, $x \geq 0$, and $y \leq -2x + 4$.

13. Find the coordinates of the vertices of the feasible region.

   F. $(0, 0), (-2, 0), (0, -4)$
   G. $(0, 0), (2, 0), (0, 4)$
   H. $(0, 0), (4, 0), (0, 2)$
   J. $(0, 0), (-4, 0), (0, 2)$ 13. _____

14. Find the maximum value of $f(x, y) = 3x + y$ for the feasible region.

   A. 2   **B.** 4   **C.** 6   **D.** 12   14. _____

15. Find the minimum value of $f(x, y) = 3x + y$ for the feasible region.

   F. 6   **G.** 4   **H.** 2   **J.** 0   15. _____

For Questions 16–18, use the following information. A college arena sells tickets to students and to the public. Student tickets are $8 each and general public tickets are $32 each. The college reserves at least 5000 tickets for students. The arena seats 18,000.

16. Let s represent the number of student tickets and p represent the number of general public tickets. Which system of inequalities represents the number of tickets sold?

   A. $s \geq 0, p \geq 0, s + p \leq 18{,}000$
   B. $s \geq 5000, p \geq 0, s + p \leq 18{,}000$
   C. $s \geq 8, p \geq 32, s + p \geq 40$
   D. $s \geq 0, p \geq 0, s + p \geq 18{,}000$ 16. _____

17. How many general public tickets should the college sell to maximize revenue (amount collected)?

   F. 18,000   **G.** 0   **H.** 13,000   **J.** 5000   17. _____

18. What is the maximum revenue?

   A. $456,000   **B.** $416,000   **C.** $40,000   **D.** $576,000   18. _____

19. What is the value of y in the solution of the system of equations?

$$2x + y + z = 13$$
$$2x - y - 3z = -3$$
$$x + 2y + 4z = 20$$

   F. 1   **G.** 2   **H.** 3   **J.** 4   19. _____

20. The 300 students at Holmes School work a total of 5000 hours each month. Each student in group A works 10 hours, each in group B works 15 hours, and each in group C works 20 hours each month. There are twice as many students in group B as in group A. Which equation would *not* be included in the system used to solve this problem?

   A. $A = 2B$
   B. $10A + 15B + 20C = 5000$
   C. $A + B + C = 300$
   D. $B = 2A$ 20. _____

Bonus Find the area of the region defined by the system of inequalities $x \geq 0, y \geq 0$, and $x + 2y \leq 4$.   **B:** _____

3 **Chapter 3 Test, Form 2A**

Write the letter for the correct answer in the blank at the right of each question.

1. The system of equations $y = -3x + 5$ and $y = -3x - 7$ has
   A. exactly one solution.
   B. no solution.
   C. infinitely many solutions.
   D. exactly two solutions.

   1. _____

Choose the correct description of each system of equations.
   F. consistent and independent
   G. inconsistent
   H. consistent and dependent
   J. inconsistent and dependent

   2. _____

2. $2x - y = 4$
   $4x - 2y = 6$

3. $9x - 3y = 15$
   $6x = 2y + 10$

   3. _____

To solve each system of equations, which expression could be substituted for y into the first equation?

4. $5x + 3y = 9$
   $4x + y = 8$
   A. $12x - 3y$
   B. $4x - 8$
   C. $-\frac{3}{5}x + 3$
   D. $8 - 4x$

   4. _____

5. $3x + 6y = 12$
   $2x - y = 5$
   F. $\frac{1}{2}y + \frac{5}{2}$
   G. $2x + 5$
   H. $2x - 5$
   J. $12y - 5$

   5. _____

6. The first equation of the system is multiplied by 3. By what number would you multiply the second equation to eliminate the x variable by adding?

   $4x - 3y = 6$
   $6x + 1y = 10$

   A. -2 B. 2 C. 9 D. -9

   6. _____

7. The first equation of the system is multiplied by 2. By what number would you multiply the second equation to eliminate the y variable by adding?

   $4x - 3y = 6$
   $6x + 1y = 10$

   F. -2 G. -1 H. 6 J. -3

   7. _____

For Questions 8 and 9, solve each system of equations.

8. $5x + 2y = 1$
   $y = 1 - 3x$
   A. $(1, -2)$
   B. $(1, 2)$
   C. $\left(0, \frac{1}{2}\right)$
   D. $(-2, 1)$

   8. _____

9. $3x + 4y = 12$
   $2x - 3y = -9$
   F. $(3, 0)$
   G. $(-1, 4)$
   H. $(4, 0)$
   J. $(0, 3)$

   9. _____

10. Which system of equations is graphed?
    A. $x + y = 5$
       $x - 2y = 2$
    C. $x - y = 5$
       $x - 2y = 2$
    B. $x + y = 5$
       $x + 2y = 2$
    D. $x - y = 5$
       $x + 2y = 2$

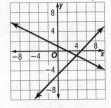

    10. _____

11. Which system of inequalities is graphed?
    F. $2x - y \geq 2$
       $x + 3y \leq 6$
    H. $2x + y > 2$
       $x - 3y \leq 6$
    G. $2x + y \geq 2$
       $x - 3y < 6$
    J. $2x - y < 2$
       $x + 3y > 6$

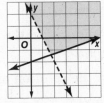

    11. _____

12. Find the coordinates of the vertices of the figure formed by the system $x \geq -1, y \geq -2$, and $2x + y \leq 6$.

     A. $(0, 0), (3, 0), (0, 6)$
     B. $(-1, 8), (-1, -2), (4, -2)$
     C. $(0, 0), (0, 3), (6, 0)$
     D. $(-1, -2), (-1, 6), (4, 0)$

12. _____

For Questions 13–15, use the system of inequalities $x \geq 2, y - x \geq -3$, and $x + y \leq 5$.

13. Find the coordinates of the vertices of the feasible region.

     F. $(2, -1), (2, 3), (4, 1)$ **H.** $(0, -3), (0, 5), (4, 1)$
     G. $(2, 0), (3, 0), (4, 1), (2, 3)$ **J.** $(0, 0), (0, 5), (3, 0), (4, 1)$

13. _____

14. Find the maximum value of $f(x, y) = x - 4y$ for the feasible region.

     A. 14   **B.** 0   **C.** 8   **D.** 6

14. _____

15. Find the minimum value of $f(x, y) = x - 4y$ for the feasible region.

     F. -2 **G.** 0   **H.** -10 **J.** -4

15. _____

16. What is the value of z in the solution of the system of equations?

     $2x + 3y + z = 9$
     $x - 2y - z = 4$
     $x - 3y + 2z = -3$

     A. 4   **B.** 1   **C.** -2 **D.** $\dfrac{3}{4}$

16. _____

An office building containing 96,000 square feet of space is to be made into apartments. There will be at most 15 one-bedroom units, each with 800 square feet of space. The remaining units, each with 1200 square feet of space, will have two bedrooms. Rent for each one-bedroom unit will be \$650 and for each two-bedroom unit will be \$900.

17. Let x represent the number of one-bedroom apartments and y represent the number of two-bedroom apartments. Which system of inequalities represents the number of apartments to be built?

     F. $x \geq 15, y \geq 0, 650x + 900y \leq 96,000$
     G. $x \leq 15, y \geq 0, 800x + 1200y \geq 96,000$
     H. $x \leq 650, y \leq 900, 800x + 1200y \leq 96,000$
     J. $0 \leq x \leq 15, y \geq 0, 800x + 1200y \leq 96,000$

17. _____

18. How many two-bedroom apartments should be built to maximize revenue?

     A. 70   **B.** 15   **C.** 80   **D.** 120

18. _____

At a university, 1200 students are enrolled in engineering. There are twice as many in electrical engineering as in mechanical engineering, and three times as many in chemical engineering as in mechanical engineering.

19. Which system of equations represents the number of students in each program?

     F. $c + m + e = 1200, 2m = e, 3m = c$ **H.** $c + m + e = 1200, 3m = e, 2m = c$
     G. $c + m + e = 1200, 2e = m, 3c = m$ **J.** $c + m + e = 1200, 2m = e, 3m = 2e$

19. _____

20. How many students are enrolled in the mechanical engineering program?

     A. 200   **B.** 400   **C.** 600   **D.** 1200

20. _____

Bonus Find the value of x in the solution of the system of equations $x + y = \dfrac{9}{8}$ and $x - 2y = \dfrac{9}{8}$.

     B: _____

3   Chapter 3 Test, Form 2B

Write the letter for the correct answer in the blank at the right of each question.

1. The system of equations $y = 2x - 3$ and $y = 4x - 3$ has

   A. exactly one solution.   **C.** infinitely many solutions.

   B. no solution.   **D.** exactly two solutions.   1. _____

Choose the correct description of each system of equations.

   F. consistent and independent   **H.** consistent and dependent

   G. inconsistent   **J.** inconsistent and dependent   2. _____

2. $x + 2y = 7$ 3. $2x + 3y = 10$
   $3x - 2y = 5$ $4x + 6y = 20$ 3. _____

To solve each system of equations, which expression could be substituted for x into the first equation?

4. $3x - 5y = 14$ **A.** $10 - 4y$ **C.** $4y + 10$
   $x + 4y = 10$ **B.** $\frac{1}{4}x + \frac{5}{2}$ **D.** $-\frac{1}{4}x + \frac{5}{2}$ 4. _____

5. $2x + 7y = 10$ **F.** $\frac{1}{2}x + 15$ **H.** $\frac{1}{2}x - 15$
   $x - 2y = 15$ **G.** $2y + 15$ **J.** $2y - 15$ 5. _____

6. The first equation of the system is multiplied by 2. $6x - 5y = 21$
   By what number would you multiply the second $4x + 7y = 15$
   equation to eliminate the x variable by adding?

   A. 3   **B.** -3 **C.** 2   **D.** -2 6. _____

7. The first equation of the system is multiplied by 4. $2x + 5y = 16$
   By what number would you multiply the second $8x - 4y = 10$
   equation to eliminate the y variable by adding?

   F. 5   **G.** -5 **H.** 2   **J.** -2 7. _____

For Questions 8 and 9, solve each system of equations.

8. $4x - 3y = 14$ **A.** $(1, 1)$ **C.** $(5, 2)$
   $y = -3x + 4$ **B.** $(-4, -10)$ **D.** $(2, -2)$ 8. _____

9. $4x - 3y = 8$ **F.** $(-2, 1)$ **H.** $(2, 0)$
   $2x + 5y = -9$ **G.** $(0, -83)$ **J.** $\left(\frac{1}{2}, -2\right)$ 9. _____

10. Which system of equations is graphed?

    A. $2x + y = 1$ **C.** $2x + y = 1$
    $-3x - y = 3$ $3x - y = 3$

    B. $2x + y = -1$ **D.** $2x + y = -1$
    $3x - y = 3$ $-3x - y = 3$

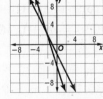

10. _____

11. Which system of inequalities is graphed?

    F. $2x + y \geq 5$ **H.** $2x - y \leq 5$
    $3x + 2y \leq 9$ $3x + 2y < 9$

    G. $2x + y > -5$ **J.** $-2x + y > 5$
    $3x - 2y \geq 9$ $3x - 2y \leq 9$

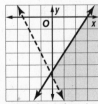

11. _____

12. Find the coordinates of the vertices of the figure formed by the system $x \geq 0, y \geq -2$, and $2x + y \leq 4$.
   A. $(3, -2), (0, 4), (0, -2)$ **C.** $(0, 0), (0, 4), (2, 0)$
   B. $(-2, 0), (4, 0), (-2, 3)$ **D.** $(-2, 3), (0, 4), (0, -2)$ **12.** _____

For Questions 13–15, use the system of inequalities $y \geq 1, y - x \leq 6$, and $x + 2y \leq 6$.

13. Find the coordinates of the vertices of the feasible region.
   F. $(-6, 0), (-2, 4), (6, 0)$ **H.** $(-5, 1), (-2, 4), (4, 1)$
   G. $(0, 1), (0, 3), (4, 1)$ **J.** $(-5, 1), (-2, 4), (0, 3), (0, 1)$ **13.** _____

14. Find the maximum value of $f(x, y) = 2x + y$ for the feasible region.
   A. 0   **B.** 11   **C.** 9   **D.** 8   **14.** _____

15. Find the minimum value of $f(x, y) = 2x + y$ for the feasible region.
   F. -10 **G.** 0   **H.** -9 **J.** -4 **15.** _____

16. What is the value of z in the solution of the system of equations?

$$2x + 3y - z = 12$$
$$4x - y + z = -3$$
$$-2x + 2y + z = 3$$

   A. -1 **B.** 12   **C.** 3   **D.** -2 **16.** _____

Tickets to a golf tournament are sold in advance for $40 each, and on the day of the event for $50 each. For the tournament to occur, at least 2000 of the 8000 tickets must be sold in advance.

17. Let a represent the number of advance tickets sold and d represent the number sold on the day of the tournament. Which system of inequalities represents the number of tickets sold?
   F. $a \geq 2000, d \geq 0, a + d \leq 8000$ **H.** $a \geq 0, d \geq 0, a + d \leq 8000$
   G. $a \geq 0, d \geq 0, a + d \leq 2000$ **J.** $a \leq 40, d \leq 50, a + d \leq 2000$ **17.** _____

18. How many advance tickets should be sold to maximize revenue?
   A. 6000   **B.** 2000   **C.** 4000   **D.** 8000   **18.** _____

A local gas station sells low-grade (ℓ), mid-grade (m), and premium (p) gasoline. Mid-grade gasoline costs $0.10 per gallon more than low-grade, and premium gasoline costs $0.10 per gallon more than mid-grade gasoline. Five gallons of low-grade gas cost $9.

19. Which system of equations represents the cost of each type of gasoline?
   F. $5\ell + m = 9, m = \ell + 0.10, p = m + 0.10$
   G. $5\ell = 9, m = \ell - 0.10, p = m - 0.10$
   H. $5\ell = 9, m = \ell + 0.10, p = m + 0.10$
   J. $0.10\ell + 0.10m + 5p = 9, 0.10\ell + m = 0, 0.10m + p = 0$ **19.** _____

20. What is the cost of one gallon of premium gasoline?
   A. $1.80   **B.** $1.90   **C.** $2.00   **D.** $2.10   **20.** _____

Bonus Solve the system of equations.

$$a + b = 6 \qquad c + d = 4 \qquad f + a = 2$$
$$b + c = 5 \qquad d + f = 3$$

   B: _____

3 Chapter 3 Test, Form 2C

Solve each system of equations by graphing.

1. $3x - 2y = 6$
$2x + y = 4$

1.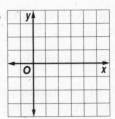

2. $3x - y = 1$
$3y = 9x + 6$

2.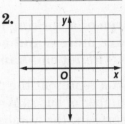

Describe each system of equations as *consistent and independent*, *consistent and dependent*, or *inconsistent*.

3. $y = 2x + 5$
$y = -3x + 4$

4. $2x - y = 5$
$6x - 3y = 15$

3. _____

4. _____

Solve each system of equations by using substitution.

5. $3x + 7y = 19$
$x + y = 5$

6. $x + 3y = 12$
$5x + y = 4$

5. _____

6. _____

Solve each system of equations by using elimination.

7. $3x - 2y = 4$
$2x + 3y = 7$

8. $4x - y = 10$
$5x + 2y = 6$

7. _____

8. _____

Solve each system of inequalities by graphing.

9. $4x - 3y < 9$
$2x + y \geq 5$

9.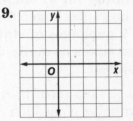

10. $y \leq \dfrac{3}{2}x - 2$
$2y \geq x - 4$

10.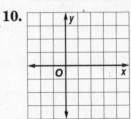

Find the coordinates of the vertices of the figure formed by each system of inequalities.

11. $y \geq -3$
$y \leq 2x + 1$
$x \leq 2$

12. $x \leq 3$
$y \leq 2x + 4$
$x + y \geq -2$
$3y \leq -2x + 12$

11. _____

12. _____

3 Chapter 3 Test, Form 2C (continued)

Use the system of inequalities $x \geq -2$, $x + y \leq 7$, and $y \geq 2x + 1$.

13. Find the coordinates of the vertices of the feasible region.

13. _____

14. Find the maximum and minimum values of the function $f(x, y) = 3x - y$ for the feasible region.

14. _____

The area of a parking lot is 600 square meters. A car requires 6 square meters and a bus requires 30 square meters of space. The lot can handle a maximum of 60 vehicles.

15. Let c represent the number of cars and b represent the number of buses. Write a system of inequalities to represent the number of vehicles that can be parked.

15. _____

16. If a car costs $3 and a bus costs $8 to park in the lot, determine the number of each vehicle to maximize the amount collected.

16. _____

Solve each system of equations.

17. $x + 2y - 3z = 5$
    $x - y + 2z = -3$
    $x + y - z = 2$

17. _____

18. $3x + y + 2z = 1$
    $2x - y + z = -3$
    $x + y - 4z = -3$

18. _____

A printing company sells small packages of personalized stationery for $7 each, medium packages for $12 each, and large packages for $15 each. Yesterday, the company sold 9 packages of stationery, collecting a total of $86. Three times as many medium packages were sold as large packages.

19. Let s represent the number of small packages, m the number of medium packages, and ℓ the number of large packages. Write a system of three equations that represents the number of packages sold.

19. _____

20. Find the number of each size package sold.

20. _____

Bonus Find the perimeter of the region defined by the system of inequalities:
   $-2 \leq x \leq 5$
   $-4 \leq y \leq -1$

B: _____

3 Chapter 3 Test, Form 2D

Solve each system of equations by graphing.

1. $x + y = 5$
$2y = x - 2$

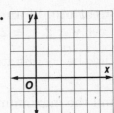

2. $y = \frac{2}{3}x - 1$
$2x + y = -1$

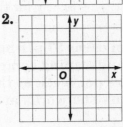

Describe each system of equations as *consistent and independent*, *consistent and dependent*, or *inconsistent*.

3. $3x - 4y = 5$
$6x - 8y = -5$

4. $2x - 7y = 14$
$x + 3y = 6$

3. _____

4. _____

Solve each system of equations by using substitution.

5. $4x - y = 10$
$y = 3x - 6$

6. $x - y = 6$
$3x + 2y = -22$

5. _____

6. _____

Solve each system of equations by using elimination.

7. $5x + 2y = 1$
$2x + 3y = 7$

8. $5x - 3y = 16$
$2x + 7y = -10$

7. _____

8. _____

Solve each system of inequalities by graphing.

9. $2x - 3y \geq -3$
$3y > -2x - 6$

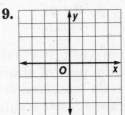

10. $x + 3y \geq 6$
$y < \frac{3}{2}x - 2$

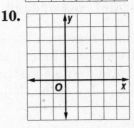

Find the coordinates of the vertices of the figure formed by the solution of each system of inequalities.

11. $x \geq -3$
$y \geq -2$
$2x + y \leq -2$

12. $y \leq 3$
$4y \leq 3x + 12$
$x + y \geq -4$
$y \geq 2x - 1$

11. _____

12. _____

Assessment

For Questions 13 and 14, use the system of inequalities
$y \leq 7, x + y \geq 2, y \geq 2x + 5.$

13. Find the coordinates of the vertices of the feasible region.

13. _____

14. Find the maximum and minimum values of the function
$f(x, y) = 3x + y$ for the feasible region.

14. _____

**Kristin earns \$7 per hour at a video store and \$10 per hour
at a landscaping company. She must work at least
4 hours per week at the video store, but the total number
of hours she works at both jobs cannot be greater than 15.**

15. Let v represent the number of hours working at the video
store and ℓ represent the number of hours working at the
landscaping company. Write a system of inequalities to
represent the number of hours worked in one week.

15. _____

16. Determine Kristin's maximum weekly earnings (before
deductions).

16. _____

Solve each system of equations.

17. $2x + y + z = 4$
$3x - y + 4z = 11$
$x - y + 5z = 20$

17. _____

18. $3x - y - z = 12$
$2x + 3y + z = 5$
$x + 2y - z = 9$

18. _____

**The price of a sweatshirt at a local shop is twice the
price of a pair of shorts. The price of a T-shirt at the
shop is \$4 less than the price of a pair of shorts. Brad
purchased 3 sweatshirts, 2 pairs of shorts, and 5 T-shirts
for a total cost of \$136.**

19. Let w represent the price of one sweatshirt, t represent the
price of one T-shirt, and h represent the price of one pair of
shorts. Write a system of three equations that represents
the prices of the clothing.

19. _____

20. Find the cost of one sweatshirt.

20. _____

Bonus Solve the system of equations.

$\frac{2}{3}x + \frac{1}{2}y = 4$ $\qquad -\frac{1}{6}x + \frac{1}{8}y = -3$

B: _____

3 Chapter 3 Test, Form 3

Solve each system of equations by graphing.

1. $\frac{1}{3}x - \frac{1}{2}y = 1$

   $\frac{1}{2}x - \frac{1}{4}y = -\frac{1}{2}$

2. $x + 0.5y = 0.5$
   $2.5 = 1.5x - y$

Describe each system of equations as *consistent and independent*, *consistent and dependent*, or *inconsistent*.

3. $2x + \frac{2}{3}y = \frac{10}{3}$
   $9x + 3y = 15$

4. $\frac{3}{14}x - \frac{1}{14}y = \frac{1}{2}$
   $6x = 2(y + 5)$

Solve each system of equations by using substitution.

5. $\frac{1}{2}x + \frac{1}{3}y = 1$

   $\frac{2}{3}y - x = 6$

6. $\frac{4}{5}a + b + \frac{3}{4} = 0$

   $2a = \frac{5}{4} - \frac{5}{2}b$

Solve each system of equations by using elimination.

7. $\frac{2}{3}x + 4y = -1$

   $\frac{1}{2}x - 3y = -\frac{9}{4}$

8. $0.2c + 1.5d = -2.7$
   $1.2c - 0.5d = 2.8$

Solve each system of inequalities by graphing.

9. $x + y \le 5$
   $x + y > -3$
   $x - 2y \le 6$
   $x - 2y \ge -2$

10. $|x| \le 1$
    $|y + 1| \le 3$
    $x + 3y > -6$

Find the coordinates of the vertices of the figure formed by the solution of each system of inequalities.

11. $x \le 2$
    $-4 \le y \le 3$
    $x + y \ge -3$

12. $-2 \le x \le 5$
    $\frac{1}{2}x + \frac{1}{2}y \le 1$
    $2x + y \ge -2$
    $y \ge -4$

1.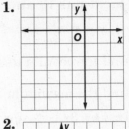

2.

3. _____

4. _____

5. _____

6. _____

7. _____

8. _____

9.

10.

11. _____

12. _____

For Questions 13 and 14, use the system of inequalities
$x \geq -3$, $x - y \geq -4$, $x \leq y + 1$, and $\frac{1}{3}x + \frac{1}{2}y \leq 2$.

13. Find the coordinates of the vertices of the feasible region.

13. _____

14. Find the maximum and minimum values of the function
$f(x, y) = 3x - \frac{1}{2}y$ for the feasible region.

14. _____

A dog food manufacturer wants to advertise its products.
A magazine charges $60 per ad and requires the purchase
of at least three ads. A radio station charges $150 per
commercial minute and requires the purchase of at least
four minutes. Each magazine ad reaches 12,000 people
while each commercial minute reaches 16,000 people. At
most $900 can be spent on advertising.

15. Let a represent the number of magazine ads and m represent
the number of commercial minutes. Write a system of
inequalities that represents the advertising plan for the company.

15. _____

16. How many ads and commercial minutes should be purchased
to reach the most people? How many people would this be?

16. _____

Solve each system of equations.

17. $4x - 6y + z = 1$

$3x + \frac{1}{2}y - \frac{2}{3}z = \frac{9}{2}$

$5x - 3y + 2z = -\frac{11}{2}$

18. $10a + b - \frac{1}{3}c = -6$

$2a - 3b + \frac{1}{7}c = \frac{32}{5}$

$-\frac{5}{2}a + \frac{1}{4}c = \frac{19}{4}$

17. _____

18. _____

An electronic repair shop offers three types of service:
on-site, at-store, and by-mail. On-site service costs 3 times
as much as at-store service. By-mail service costs $10 less
than at-store service. Last week, the shop completed
15 services on-site, 40 services at-store, and 5 services by
mail for total sales of $2650.

19. Let s represent the cost of one on-site repair, a represent
the cost of one at-store repair, and m represent the cost of
one by-mail repair service. Write a system of three equations
that represents the cost of each repair service.

19. _____

20. Determine the cost of one on-site repair service.

20. _____

Bonus Solve the system of equations.

$\frac{3}{x} + \frac{4}{y} = \frac{5}{2}$

$\frac{6}{x} - \frac{1}{y} = \frac{1}{2}$

B: _____

3   Chapter 3 Extended-Response Test

Demonstrate your knowledge by giving a clear, concise solution to each problem. Be sure to include all relevant drawings and justify your answers. You may show your solution in more than one way or investigate beyond the requirements of the problem.

1. The square of Janet's age is 400 more than the square of the sum of Kim's and Sue's ages. Kim's and Sue's ages total 10 less than Janet's age. Find the square of the sum of the ages of Janet, Kim, and Sue. Explain your reasoning.

2. A feasible region has vertices at $(0, 8)$, $(6, 0)$, and $(0, 0)$.
   a. Write a system of inequalities whose graph forms this feasible region.
   b. Explain how to find the maximum and minimum values of $f(x, y) = x - y$ for the region.

3. Explain what the algebraic solution of a system of two linear equations is and what that means in terms of the graphs of the equations of the system.

4. When describing a system of two linear equations, a student indicated that the system was inconsistent and dependent. Discuss the meaning of the student's description. Then assess the student's understanding of these terms.

5. A business owner asks the company finance manager to develop a formula, or function, for the cost incurred in the production of their products, and another function for the revenue (money collected) that the company earns when the products are sold. In preparing the report for the owner, the finance manager prepares a graph which shows both the cost function and the revenue function. The business owner, on seeing the graph of two parallel lines, makes a major business decision. What might that decision be and why would it be made?

6. Explain what it means for a system of two linear inequalities to have no solution. Sketch a graph of such a system and write the system of inequalities represented by your graph.

Assessment

3 Standardized Test Practice
(Chapters 1–3)

Part 1: Multiple Choice

Instructions: Fill in the appropriate circle for the best answer.

1. A number is 8 more than the ratio of q and 2. What is three-fourths of the number in terms of q?

   A 6   **B** $5 + \frac{3q}{8}$ **C** $\frac{3q}{8}$ **D** $6 + \frac{3q}{8}$ 1. Ⓐ Ⓑ Ⓒ Ⓓ

2. Carlisle's salary was raised from $19,000 to $23,750. Find the percent of increase.

   F 20%   **G** 25%   **H** 30%   **J** 47.5%   2. Ⓕ Ⓖ Ⓗ Ⓙ

3. Which of the following is the additive inverse of $-\frac{2}{7}$?

   A $\frac{2}{7}$ **B** $\frac{2}{8}$ **C** $\frac{7}{2}$ **D** $-\frac{7}{2}$ 3. Ⓐ Ⓑ Ⓒ Ⓓ

4. What is the slope of the line that passes through $(1, -4)$ and $(-1, 2)$?

   F $m = 3$ **G** $m = 2$ **H** $m = 1$ **J** $m = -3$ 4. Ⓕ Ⓖ Ⓗ Ⓙ

5. Solve $|x - 15| = 6$.

   A $\{21, -9\}$ **B** $\{-21, 9\}$ **C** $\{9, 21\}$ **D** $\{-21, -9\}$ 5. Ⓐ Ⓑ Ⓒ Ⓓ

6. The formula for the area A of a triangle is $A = \frac{1}{2}bh$, where b represents the base and h represents the height. Find the area of the triangle at the right.

   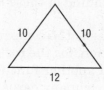

   F 24   **H** 48

   G 60   **J** 120   6. Ⓕ Ⓖ Ⓗ Ⓙ

7. If m is an integer greater than 5, then which of the following must represent an odd integer?

   A m^2 **B** $m - 1$ **C** $2m - 3$ **D** $m + 2$ 7. Ⓐ Ⓑ Ⓒ Ⓓ

8. Desiree and Mario together have $30. Mario and Scott together have $26. Desiree and Scott together have $34. What is the least amount of money any of them has?

   F $11   **G** $15   **H** $19   **J** $26   8. Ⓕ Ⓖ Ⓗ Ⓙ

9. If $x, y,$ and z are negative integers, which of the following must be true?

   A $x(y + z) < 0$ **C** $x - (y - z) < 0$

   B $xyz < 0$ **D** $x < y - z$ 9. Ⓐ Ⓑ Ⓒ Ⓓ

10. If $\frac{r + 2}{r} = \frac{4}{3}$, then $\frac{r}{2} =$ _____.

   F $\frac{1}{4}$ **G** $\frac{2}{3}$ **H** 1   **J** 3   10. Ⓕ Ⓖ Ⓗ Ⓙ

3 Standardized Test Practice
(Chapters 1–3)

For Questions 11–12, use the table that shows the years of experience for six store clerks and their current weekly salary.

Years	2	3	4	3	1	5
Salary	260	320	380	320	200	440

11. Which could be a prediction for the data?

    A $y = 60x + 140$ **C** $y = 60x - 140$

    B $y = 30x + 100$ **D** $y = -60x + 140$ **11.** Ⓐ Ⓑ Ⓒ Ⓓ

12. Which best predicts the weekly salary of a store clerk with 6 years of experience?

    F $445   **H** $500

    G $450   **J** $600   **12.** Ⓕ Ⓖ Ⓗ Ⓙ

13. Which characteristic belongs to the graphs of $2y = 5x + 1$ and $5y = -2x + 1$?

    A the same y-intercept   **C** perpendicular lines

    B the same x-intercept   **D** parallel lines   **13.** Ⓐ Ⓑ Ⓒ Ⓓ

14. Let p represent the price Noah charges for singing at a wedding. Let $f(x)$ represent the total amount of money that Noah makes for singing at x weddings. The function $f(x)$ is best represented by?

    F $x + p$ **G** xp **H** $x^2 p$ **J** $x(p + 1)$ **14.** Ⓕ Ⓖ Ⓗ Ⓙ

15. Which is the solution for the following system of equations?

$$x + 2y + z = 20$$
$$2x + y - z = 7$$
$$3x - 2y + 2z = 14$$

    A $(-4, -5, 34)$ **B** $(4, -5, 26)$ **C** $(5, 6, 3)$ **D** $(4, 5, 6)$ **15.** Ⓐ Ⓑ Ⓒ Ⓓ

Part 2: Grid In

Instructions: Enter your answer by writing each digit of the answer in a column box and then shading in the appropriate circle that corresponds to that entry.

16. In a survey of high school sophomores, 60 students named Science as their favorite subject. If 70% of the students surveyed had a favorite subject other than Science, how many sophomores were surveyed?

16.

⓪	⓪	⓪	⓪		⓪	⓪	⓪
①	①	①	①		①	①	①
②	②	②	②		②	②	②
③	③	③	③		③	③	③
④	④	④	④		④	④	④
⑤	⑤	⑤	⑤		⑤	⑤	⑤
⑥	⑥	⑥	⑥		⑥	⑥	⑥
⑦	⑦	⑦	⑦		⑦	⑦	⑦
⑧	⑧	⑧	⑧		⑧	⑧	⑧
⑨	⑨	⑨	⑨		⑨	⑨	⑨

17.

⓪	⓪	⓪	⓪		⓪	⓪	⓪
①	①	①	①		①	①	①
②	②	②	②		②	②	②
③	③	③	③		③	③	③
④	④	④	④		④	④	④
⑤	⑤	⑤	⑤		⑤	⑤	⑤
⑥	⑥	⑥	⑥		⑥	⑥	⑥
⑦	⑦	⑦	⑦		⑦	⑦	⑦
⑧	⑧	⑧	⑧		⑧	⑧	⑧
⑨	⑨	⑨	⑨		⑨	⑨	⑨

17. If figure $RSTV$ is a parallelogram, what is the value of x?

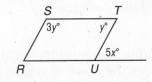

3 ## Chapter 3 Standardized Test Practice *(continued)*
(Chapters 1–3)

Part 3: Short Answer

Instructions: Write your answers in the space provided.

18. Simplify $\frac{1}{3}(6x - 21) - 4(x + 5)$.

18. _____

19. Solve $7 - 2(m + 3) = 4 - m$.

19. _____

20. Solve the inequality $|\,3 + 2x\,| > 7$. Then graph the solution set.

20. _____

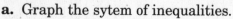
-6-5-4-3-2-1 0 1 2 3

21. Find $f(2a)$ if $f(x) = -x^3 + 2x - 5$.

21. _____

For Questions 22 and 23, state whether each equation or function is linear. If not, explain.

22. $f(x) = \frac{1}{x} + 5$ 23. $y + x^2 = 2$

22. _____

23. _____

24. Write an equation for the line that passes through $(2, -3)$ and is parallel to the line whose equation is $y = -4x + 3$.

24. _____

25. Evaluate $f\left(\frac{1}{8}\right)$ if $f(x) = 5 - 3x$.

25. _____

26. Describe the system of equations as *consistent and independent*, *consistent and dependent*, or *inconsistent*.
$2x - 3y = 11$
$4x + 6y = 22$

26. _____

27. Solve the system of equations by using substitution.
$y = 2x + 5$
$4x - 5y = -1$

27. _____

28. Solve the system of equations by using elimination.
$y - 3x = 5$
$4x - 9y = -22$

28. _____

29. Solve the system of equations.
$2x + y - 3z = 9$
$x - 2y + z = -8$
$x + 3y - 2z = 11$

29. _____

30a.

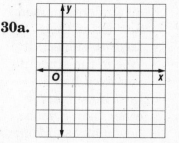

30. The inequalities $x \geq 1$, $y \geq -2$, and $x + y \leq 4$, represent the constraints on a problem Benjamin is solving.
   a. Graph the sytem of inequalities.

   b. Find the coordinates of the vertices of the figure formed by the system of inequalities.

30b. _____

   c. Find the maximum and minimum values of the function $f(x, y) = y - 3x$ for the feasible region.

30c. _____

3-1 Lesson Reading Guide

Solving Systems of Equations by Graphing

Get Ready for the Lesson

Read the introduction to Lesson 3-1 in your textbook.

- Which are growing faster, in-store sales or online sales? **online sales**

- In what year is the in-store and online sales the same? **2005**

Read the Lesson

1. The Study Tip on page 117 of your textbook says that when you solve a system of equations by graphing and find a point of intersection of the two lines, you must always check the ordered pair in *both* of the original equations. Why is it not good enough to check the ordered pair in just one of the equations?

   Sample answer: To be a solution of the system, the ordered pair must make both of the equations true.

2. Under each system graphed below, write all of the following words that apply: *consistent, inconsistent, dependent,* and *independent.*

   inconsistent   **consistent; dependent**   **consistent; independent**

Remember What You Learned

3. Look up the words *consistent* and *inconsistent* in a dictionary. How can the meaning of these words help you distinguish between consistent and inconsistent systems of equations?

   Sample answer: One meaning of *consistent* is "being in agreement," or "compatible," while one meaning of *inconsistent* is "not being in agreement" or "incompatible." When a system is consistent, the equations are compatible because both can be true at the same time (for the same values of *x* and *y*). When a system is inconsistent, the equations are incompatible because they can never be true at the same time.

---

3 Anticipation Guide

Systems of Equations and Inequalities

STEP 1   *Before you begin Chapter 3*

- Read each statement.

- Decide whether you Agree (A) or Disagree (D) with the statement.

- Write A or D in the first column OR if you are not sure whether you agree or disagree, write NS (Not Sure).

STEP 1 A, D, or NS	Statement	STEP 2 A or D
	1. A system of equations consists of two or more equations with different variables.	D
	2. The solution of a system of equations can be found by finding the intersection of the graphs of the equations.	A
	3. A system of equations that is inconsistent has an infinite number of solutions.	D
	4. Given the two equations $y = x - 7$ and $3x + 4y = 10$, a solution can be found by substituting $x - 7$ for y in the second equation.	A
	5. The product of the equation $6m - 4n = 22$ and -2 is $-12m + 8n = 22$.	D
	6. When solving a system of inequalities by graphing, if the graphs do not intersect then there is no solution.	A
	7. All the ordered pairs in the intersection of the graphs of a system of inequalities are called constraints.	D
	8. If the intersection of the graphs of a system of inequalities is a polygonal region, that region is called bounded.	A
	9. Linear programming is the process of finding all solutions to a system of linear inequalities.	D
	10. The solution to a system of equations with three variables is written as (x, y, z) and is called an ordered triple.	A

STEP 2   *After you complete Chapter 3*

- Reread each statement and complete the last column by entering an A or a D.

- Did any of your opinions about the statements change from the first column?

- For those statements that you mark with a D, use a piece of paper to write an example of why you disagree.

Answers (Lesson 3-1)

3-1 Study Guide and Intervention

NAME _____ DATE _____ PERIOD _____

Solving Systems of Equations by Graphing

Graph Systems of Equations A system of equations is a set of two or more equations containing the same variables. You can solve a system of linear equations by graphing the equations on the same coordinate plane. If the lines intersect, the solution is that intersection point.

Example Solve the system of equations by graphing.

$$x - 2y = 4 \qquad x + y = -2$$

Write each equation in slope-intercept form.

$$x - 2y = 4 \quad \rightarrow \quad y = \frac{x}{2} - 2$$
$$x + y = -2 \quad \rightarrow \quad y = -x - 2$$

The graphs appear to intersect at $(0, -2)$.

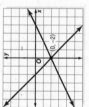

CHECK Substitute the coordinates into each equation.

$$\begin{array}{ll} x - 2y = 4 & x + y = -2 \\ 0 - 2(-2) \stackrel{?}{=} 4 & 0 + (-2) \stackrel{?}{=} -2 \\ 4 = 4 \checkmark & -2 = -2 \checkmark \end{array}$$

The solution of the system is $(0, -2)$.

Exercises

Solve each system of equations by graphing.

1. $y = -\dfrac{x}{3} + 1$

$y = \dfrac{x}{2} - 4$ **(6, −1)**

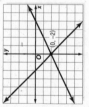

2. $y = 2x - 2$

$y = -x + 4$ **(2, 2)**

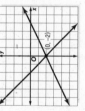

3. $y = -\dfrac{x}{2} + 3$

$y = \dfrac{x}{4}$ **(4, 1)**

4. $3x - y = 0$

$x - y = -2$ **(1, 3)**

5. $2x + \dfrac{y}{3} = -7$

$\dfrac{x}{2} + y = 1$ **(−4, 3)**

6. $\dfrac{x}{2} - y = 2$

$2x - y = -1$ **(−2, −3)**

Chapter 3 — 6 — *Glencoe Algebra 2*

3-1 Study Guide and Intervention *(continued)*

NAME _____ DATE _____ PERIOD _____

Solving Systems of Equations by Graphing

Classify Systems of Equations The following chart summarizes the possibilities for graphs of two linear equations in two variables.

Graphs of Equations	Slopes of Lines	Classification of System	Number of Solutions
Lines intersect	Different slopes	Consistent and independent	One
Lines coincide (same line)	Same slope, same y-intercept	Consistent and dependent	Infinitely many
Lines are parallel	Same slope, different y-intercepts	Inconsistent	None

Example Graph the system of equations and describe it as *consistent and independent, consistent and dependent, or inconsistent.*

Write each equation in slope-intercept form.

$$x - 3y = 6 \quad \rightarrow \quad y = \frac{1}{3}x - 2$$
$$2x - y = -3 \quad \rightarrow \quad y = 2x + 3$$

The graphs intersect at $(-3, -3)$. Since there is one solution, the system is consistent and independent.

$$x - 3y = 6$$
$$2x - y = -3$$

Exercises

Graph the system of equations and describe it as *consistent and independent, consistent and dependent, or inconsistent.*

1. $3x + y = -2$

$6x + 2y = 10$ **inconsistent**

2. $x + 2y = 5$

$3x - 15 = -6y$ **consistent and dependent**

3. $2x - 3y = 0$

$4x - 6y = 3$ **inconsistent**

4. $2x - y = 3$

$x + 2y = 4$ **consistent and independent**

5. $4x + y = -2$

$2x + \dfrac{y}{2} = -1$ **consistent and dependent**

6. $3x - y = 2$

$x + y = 6$ **consistent and independent**

Chapter 3 — 7 — *Glencoe Algebra 2*

Practice

NAME _____ DATE _____ PERIOD _____

3-1

Lesson 3-1

Solving Systems of Equations By Graphing

Solve each system of equations by graphing.

1. $x - 2y = 0$
$y = 2x - 3$ **(2, 1)**
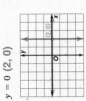

2. $x + 2y = 4$
$2x - 3y = 1$ **(2, 1)**
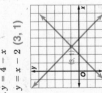

3. $2x + y = 3$
$y = \frac{1}{2}x - \frac{9}{2}$ **(3, −3)**

4. $y - x = 3$
$y = 1$ **(−2, 1)**

5. $2x - y = 6$
$x + 2y = -2$ **(2, −2)**

6. $5x - y = 4$
$-2x + 6y = 4$ **(1, 1)**

Graph each system of equations and describe it as consistent and independent, consistent and dependent, or inconsistent.

7. $2x - y = 4$
$x - y = 2$ **consistent and indep.**

8. $y = -x - 2$
$x + y = -4$ **inconsistent**

9. $2y - 8 = x$
$y = \frac{1}{2}x + 4$ **consistent and dep.**

SOFTWARE For Exercises 10–12, use the following information.
Location Mapping needs new software. Software A costs $13,000 plus $500 per additional site license. Software B costs $2500 plus $1200 per additional site license.

10. Write two equations that represent the cost of each software. A: $y = 13{,}000 + 500x$, B: $y = 2500 + 1200x$

11. Graph the equations. Estimate the break-even point of the software costs. **15 additional licenses**

12. If Location Mapping plans to buy 10 additional site licenses, which software will cost less? **B**

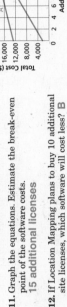

Software Costs

Chapter 3 **9** Glencoe Algebra 2

Skills Practice

NAME _____ DATE _____ PERIOD _____

3-1

Solving Systems of Equations By Graphing

Solve each system of equations by graphing.

1. $x = 2$
$y = 0$ **(2, 0)**

2. $y = -3x + 6$
$y = 2x - 4$ **(2, 0)**

3. $y = 4 - 3x$
$y = -\frac{1}{2}x - 1$ **(2, −2)**

4. $y = 4 - x$
$y = x - 2$ **(3, 1)**
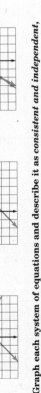

5. $y = -2x + 2$
$y = \frac{1}{3}x - 5$ **(3, −4)**
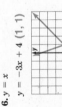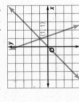

6. $y = x$
$y = -3x + 4$ **(1, 1)**
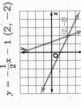

7. $x + y = 3$
$x - y = 1$ **(2, 1)**

8. $x - y = 4$
$2x - 5y = 8$ **(4, 0)**
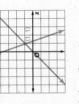

9. $3x - 2y = 4$
$2x - y = 1$ **(−2, −5)**

Graph each system of equations and describe it as consistent and independent, consistent and dependent, or inconsistent.

10. $y = -3x$
$y = -3x + 2$ **inconsistent**

11. $y = x - 5$
$-2x + 2y = -10$ **consistent and dependent**

12. $2x - 5y = 10$
$3x + y = 15$ **consistent and independent**

Chapter 3 **8** Glencoe Algebra 2

NAME _____ DATE _____ PERIOD _____

3-1 Enrichment

Solutions to Nonlinear Equations

Real-life situations are often not capable of being represented by a linear equation. Systems of nonlinear equations are often used in the study of population dynamics, modeling carbon monoxide exposure, and determining the height of an object in free fall. **Nonlinear equations** have one variable raised to a power other than one or multiplication of two or more variables.

Examples

a. $xy = 1$ or $y = \dfrac{1}{x}$ The first equation has a product of two variables.
The second is the same equation solved for y.

b. $y = x^3 - 2x + 1$ The variable x is raised to the third power.

Systems of nonlinear equations consist of two or more equations, where at least one is nonlinear.

Solutions to these systems are typically difficult to find. One useful method for finding solutions to systems of nonlinear equations is the same as the method for finding solutions to systems of linear equations—use technology to graph the system and find the point(s) of intersection. The graph of the system is shown at the right.

$$\begin{cases} y = \dfrac{1}{x} \\ y = x^3 - 2x + 1 \end{cases}$$

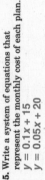

Using the Intersection function of a graphing calculator you find that one point of intersection is approximately (1.34509, 0.743445).

Exercises

1. Use a graphing calculator to find the other point of intersection.
(−1.71064, −0.584575)

2. Use the **Zoom** feature on the calculator to zoom in around the point of intersection. What do the two nonlinear equations remind you of at this level of zoom? They should appear to be linear.

3. **GOLF** The height of a golf ball dropped from the top of a 100-foot tower after t seconds is given by $h = -16t^3 + 100$. Use a graphing calculator to determine when (in seconds) the golf ball is 10 feet from the ground.
2.37171 seconds

Chapter 3   11   *Glencoe Algebra 2*

NAME _____ DATE _____ PERIOD _____

3-1 Word Problem Practice

Solving Systems of Equations By Graphing

1. **STREETS** Andrew is studying a map and notices two streets that run parallel to each other. He computes the equations of the lines that represent the two roads. Are these two equations *consistent* or *inconsistent*? If they are consistent, are they *independent* or *dependent*? Explain.
They are inconsistent. Parallel lines never intersect so there is no solution.

2. **SPOTLIGHTS** Ship A has coordinates (−1, −2) and Ship B has coordinates (−4, 1). Both ships have their spotlights fixated on the same lifeboat. The light beam from Ship A travels along the line $y = 2x$. The light beam from Ship B travels along the line $y = x + 5$. What are the coordinates of the lifeboat?

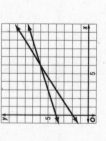

(5, 10)

3. **LASERS** A machine heats up a single point by shining several lasers at it. The equations $y = x + 1$ and $y = -x + 7$ describe two of the laser beams. Graph both of these lines to find the coordinates of the heated point

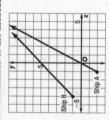

(3, 4)

4. **PATHS** The graph shows the paths of two people who took a walk in a park. Where did their paths intersect?
(6, 6)

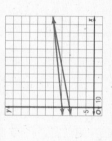

PHONE SERVICE For Exercises 5–7, use the following information.
Beth is deciding between two telephone plans. Plan A charges $15 per month plus 10 cents per minute. Plan B charges $20 per month plus 5 cents per minute.

5. Write a system of equations that represent the monthly cost of each plan.
$y = 0.1x + 15$
$y = 0.05x + 20$

6. Graph the equations.

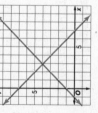

7. For how many minutes per month do the two phone plans cost the same amount?
100 minutes

Chapter 3   10   *Glencoe Algebra 2*

NAME _____ DATE _____ PERIOD _____

3-1 Spreadsheet Activity
Break-Even Point

You have learned that the break-even point is the point at which the income equals the cost. You can use the formulas and charts in a spreadsheet to find a break-even point.

Example Carly Ericson is considering opening a candle business. She estimates that she will have an annual overhead of $15,000. It costs Carly $3.00 to make a jar candle, which she sells for $12.50. What is Carly's break-even point?

Use Column A for the number of candles. Columns B and C are the cost and the income, respectively.

Extend the rows of the spreadsheet to find the point at which the income first exceeds the cost. The break-even point occurs between this point and the previous point. In this case, the break even point occurs between 1500 and 1600 candles.

The chart tool of the spreadsheet allows you to graph the data. The graph verifies the solution.

◇	A	B	C
1	Candles	Cost	Income
2	0	$15,000	$0
3	100	$15,300	$1,250
4	200	$15,600	$2,500
5	300	$15,900	$3,750
6	400	$16,200	$5,000
7	500	$16,500	$6,250
8	600	$16,800	$7,500
9	700	$17,100	$8,750
10	800	$17,400	$10,000
11	900	$17,700	$11,250
12	1000	$18,000	$12,500
13	1100	$18,300	$13,750
14	1200	$18,600	$15,000
15	1300	$18,900	$16,250
16	1400	$19,200	$17,500
17	1500	$19,500	$18,750
18	1600	$19,800	$20,000

Sheet 1 / Sheet 2 / Sheet 3

Candle Cost and Income

Exercises

1. If Carly could decrease her annual overhead to $14,000, what would the break-even point be? **between 1400 and 1500 candles**

2. Suppose Carly decreases her annual overhead to $14,000 and increases the price of a candle to $14.00. What is the new break-even point? **between 1200 and 1300 candles**

NAME _____ DATE _____ PERIOD _____

3-2 Lesson Reading Guide
Solving Systems of Equations Algebraically

Get Ready for the Lesson

Read the introduction to Lesson 3-2 in your textbook.

- How many more minutes of long distance time did Yolanda use in February than in January? **13 minutes**

- How much more were the February charges than the January charges? **$1.04**

- Using your answers for the questions above, how can you find the rate per minute? Find $1.04 ÷ 13.

Read the Lesson

1. Suppose that you are asked to solve the system of equations at the right by the substitution method.

$$4x - 5y = 7$$
$$3x + y = -9$$

The first step is to solve one of the equations for one variable in terms of the other. To make your work as easy as possible, which equation would you solve for which variable? Explain. **Sample answer: Solve the second equation for y because in that equation the variable y has a coefficient of 1.**

2. Suppose that you are asked to solve the system of equations at the right by the elimination method.

$$2x + 3y = -2$$
$$7x - y = 39$$

To make your work as easy as possible, which variable would you eliminate? Describe how you would do this. **Sample answer: Eliminate the variable y; multiply the second equation by 3 and then add the result to the first equation.**

Remember What You Learned

3. The substitution method and elimination method for solving systems both have several steps, and it may be difficult to remember them. You may be able to remember them more easily if you notice what the methods have in common. What step is the same in both methods? **Sample answer: After finding the value of one of the variables, you find the value of the other variable by substituting the value you have found in one of the original equations.**

Answers

3-2 Study Guide and Intervention

Solving Systems of Equations Algebraically

Substitution To solve a system of linear equations by **substitution**, first solve for one variable in terms of the other in one of the equations. Then substitute this expression into the other equation and simplify.

Example Use substitution to solve the system of equations.
$$2x - y = 9$$
$$x + 3y = -6$$

Solve the first equation for y in terms of x.

$2x - y = 9$	First equation
$-y = -2x + 9$	Subtract 2x from both sides.
$y = 2x - 9$	Multiply both sides by -1.

Substitute the expression $2x - 9$ for y into the second equation and solve for x.

$x + 3y = -6$	Second equation
$x + 3(2x - 9) = -6$	Substitute 2x − 9 for y.
$x + 6x - 27 = -6$	Distributive Property
$7x - 27 = -6$	Simplify.
$7x = 21$	Add 27 to each side.
$x = 3$	Divide each side by 7.

Now, substitute the value 3 for x in either original equation and solve for y.

$2x - y = 9$	First equation
$2(3) - y = 9$	Replace x with 3.
$6 - y = 9$	Simplify.
$-y = 3$	Subtract 6 from each side.
$y = -3$	Multiply each side by −1.

The solution of the system is (3, −3).

Exercises

Solve each system of linear equations by using substitution.

1. $3x + y = 7$
$4x + 2y = 16$
$(-1, 10)$

2. $2x + y = 5$
$3x - 3y = 3$
$(2, 1)$

3. $2x + 3y = -3$
$x + 2y = 2$
$(-12, 7)$

4. $2x - y = 7$
$6x - 3y = 14$
no solution

5. $4x - 3y = 4$
$2x + y = -8$
$(-2, -4)$

6. $5x + y = 6$
$3 - x = 0$
$(3, -9)$

7. $x + 8y = -2$
$x - 3y = 20$
$(14, -2)$

8. $2x - y = -4$
$4x + y = 1$
$\left(-\frac{1}{2}, 3\right)$

9. $x - y = -2$
$2x - 3y = 2$
$(-8, -6)$

10. $x - 4y = 4$
$2x + 12y = 13$
$\left(5, \frac{1}{4}\right)$

11. $x + 3y = 2$
$4x + 12y = 8$
infinitely many

12. $2x + 2y = 4$
$x - 2y = 0$
$\left(\frac{4}{3}, \frac{2}{3}\right)$

3-2 Study Guide and Intervention (continued)

Solving Systems of Equations Algebraically

Elimination To solve a system of linear equations by **elimination**, add or subtract the equations to eliminate one of the variables. You may first need to multiply one or both of the equations by a constant so that one of the variables has the same (or opposite) coefficient in one equation as it has in the other.

Example 1 Use the elimination method to solve the system of equations.
$$2x - 4y = -26$$
$$3x - y = -24$$

Multiply the second equation by 4. Then subtract the equations to eliminate the y variable.

$2x - 4y = -26$ → $2x - 4y = -26$
$3x - y = -24$ → (Multiply by 4.) $12x - 4y = -96$
$-10x = 70$
$x = -7$

Replace x with −7 and solve for y.

$2x - 4y = -26$
$2(-7) - 4y = -26$
$-14 - 4y = -26$
$-4y = -12$
$y = 3$

The solution is (−7, 3).

Example 2 Use the elimination method to solve the system of equations.
$$3x - 2y = 4$$
$$5x + 3y = -25$$

Multiply the first equation by 3 and the second equation by 2. Then add the equations to eliminate the y variable.

$3x - 2y = 4$ → (Multiply by 3.) $9x - 6y = 12$
$5x + 3y = -25$ → (Multiply by 2.) $10x + 6y = -50$
$19x = -38$
$x = -2$

Replace x with −2 and solve for y.

$3x - 2y = 4$
$3(-2) - 2y = 4$
$-6 - 2y = 4$
$-2y = 10$
$y = -5$

The solution is (−2, −5).

Exercises

Solve each system of equations by using elimination.

1. $2x - y = 7$
$3x + y = 8$
$(3, -1)$

2. $x - 2y = 4$
$-x + 6y = 12$
$(12, 4)$

3. $3x + 4y = -10$
$x - 4y = 2$
$(-2, -1)$

4. $3x - y = 12$
$5x + 2y = 20$
$(4, 0)$

5. $4x - y = 6$
$2x - \frac{y}{2} = 4$
no solution

6. $5x + 2y = 12$
$-6x - 2y = -14$
$(2, 1)$

7. $2x + y = 8$
$3x + \frac{3}{2}y = 12$
infinitely many

8. $7x + 2y = -1$
$4x - 3y = -13$
$(-1, 3)$

9. $3x + 8y = -6$
$x - y = 9$
$(6, -3)$

10. $5x + 4y = 12$
$7x - 6y = 40$
$(4, -2)$

11. $-4x + y = -12$
$4x + 2y = 6$
$\left(\frac{5}{2}, -2\right)$

12. $5m + 2n = -8$
$4m + 3n = 2$
$(-4, 6)$

3-2 Skills Practice

Solving Systems of Equations Algebraically

Solve each system of equations by using substitution.

1. $m + n = 20$
   $m - n = -4$ (8, 12)

2. $x + 3y = -3$
   $4x + 3y = 6$ (3, -2)

3. $w - z = 1$
   $2w + 3z = 12$ (3, 2)

4. $3r + s = 5$
   $2r - s = 5$ (2, -1)

5. $2b + 3c = -4$
   $b + c = 3$ (13, -10)

6. $x - y = -5$
   $3x + 4y = 13$ (-1, 4)

Solve each system of equations by using elimination.

7. $2p - q = 17$
   $3p + q = 8$ (5, -7)

8. $2j - k = 3$
   $3j + k = 2$ (1, -1)

9. $3c - 2d = 2$
   $3c + 4d = 50$ (6, 8)

10. $2f + 3g = 9$
    $f - g = 2$ (3, 1)

11. $-2x + y = -1$
    $x + 2y = 3$ (1, 1)

12. $2x - y = 12$
    $2x - y = 6$ no solution

Solve each system of equations by using either substitution or elimination.

13. $-r + t = 5$
    $-2r + t = 4$ (1, 6)

14. $2x - y = -5$
    $4x + y = 2$ $\left(-\frac{1}{2}, 4\right)$

15. $x - 3y = -12$
    $2x + y = 11$ (3, 5)

16. $2p - 3q = 6$
    $-2p + 3q = -6$ infinitely many

17. $6w - 8z = 16$
    $3w - 4z = 8$ infinitely many

18. $c + d = 6$
    $c - d = 0$ (3, 3)

19. $2u + 4v = -6$
    $u + 2v = 3$ no solution

20. $3a + b = -1$
    $-3a + b = 5$ (-1, 2)

21. $2x + y = 6$
    $3x - 2y = 16$ (4, -2)

22. $3y - z = -6$
    $-3y - z = 6$ (-2, 0)

23. $c + 2d = -2$
    $-2c - 5d = 3$ (-4, 1)

24. $3r - 2s = 1$
    $2r - 3s = 9$ (-3, -5)

25. The sum of two numbers is 12. The difference of the same two numbers is -4. Find the numbers. **4, 8**

26. Twice a number minus a second number is -1. Twice the second number added to three times the first number is 9. Find the two numbers. **1, 3**

3-2 Practice

Solving Systems of Equations Algebraically

Solve each system of equations by using substitution.

1. $2x + y = 4$
   $3x + 2y = 1$ (7, -10)

2. $x - 3y = 9$
   $x + 2y = -1$ (3, -2)

3. $g + 3h = 8$
   $\frac{1}{3}g + h = 9$ no solution

4. $2a - 4b = 6$
   $-a + 2b = -3$ infinitely many

5. $2m + n = 6$
   $5m + 6n = 1$ (5, -4)

6. $4x - 3y = -6$
   $-x - 2y = 7$ (-3, -2)

7. $u - 2v = \frac{1}{2}$
   $-u + 2v = 5$ no solution

8. $x - 3y = 16$
   $4x - y = 9$ (1, -5)

9. $w + 3z = 1$
   $3w - 5z = -4$ $\left(-\frac{1}{2}, \frac{1}{2}\right)$

Solve each system of equations by using elimination.

10. $2r + s = 5$
    $3r - s = 20$ (5, -5)

11. $2m - n = -1$
    $3m + 2n = 30$ (4, 9)

12. $6x + 3y = 6$
    $8x + 5y = 12$ (-1, 4)

13. $3j - k = 10$
    $4j - k = 16$ (6, 8)

14. $2x - y = -4$
    $-4x + 2y = 6$ no solution

15. $2g + h = 6$
    $3g - 2h = 16$ (4, -2)

16. $2t + 4v = 6$
    $-t - 2v = -3$ infinitely many

17. $3x - 2y = 12$
    $2x + \frac{2}{3}y = 14$ (6, 3)

18. $\frac{1}{2}x + 3y = 11$
    $8x - 5y = 17$ (4, 3)

Solve each system of equations by using either substitution or elimination.

19. $8x + 3y = -5$
    $10x + 6y = -13$ $\left(\frac{1}{2}, -3\right)$

20. $8q - 15r = -40$
    $4q + 2r = 56$ (10, 8)

21. $3x - 4y = 12$
    $\frac{1}{3}x - \frac{4}{9}y = \frac{4}{3}$ infinitely many

22. $4b - 2d = 5$
    $-2b + d = 1$ no solution

23. $s + 3y = 4$
    $s = 1$ (1, 1)

24. $4m - 2p = 0$
    $-3m + 9p = 5$ $\left(\frac{1}{3}, \frac{2}{3}\right)$

25. $5g + 4k = 10$
    $-3g - 5k = 7$ (6, -5)

26. $0.5x + 2y = 5$
    $x - 2y = -8$ (-2, 3)

27. $h - z = 3$
    $-3h + 3z = 6$ no solution

SPORTS For Exercises 28 and 29, use the following information.
Last year the volleyball team paid $5 per pair for socks and $17 per pair for shorts on a total purchase of $315. This year they spent $342 to buy the same number of pairs of socks and shorts because the socks now cost $6 a pair and the shorts cost $18.

28. Write a system of two equations that represents the number of pairs of socks and shorts bought each year. $5x + 17y = 315$, $6x + 18y = 342$

29. How many pairs of socks and shorts did the team buy each year? **socks: 12, shorts: 15**

Lesson 3-2

3-2 Word Problem Practice

Solving Systems of Equations Algebraically

1. SUPPLIES Kirsta and Arthur both need pens and blank CDs. The equation that represents Kirsta's purchases is $y = 27 - 3x$. The equation that represents Arthur's purchases is $y = 17 - x$. If x represents the price of the pens, and y represents the prices of the CDs, what are the prices of the pens and the CDs?
pens are $5 a pack, CDs are $12 a pack

2. WALKING Amy is walking a straight path that can be represented by the equation $y = 2x + 3$. At the same time Kendra is walking the straight path that has the equation $3y = 6x + 6$. What is the solution to the system of equations that represents the paths the two girls walked? Explain.
There is no solution. Their paths never cross.

3. CAFETERIA To furnish a cafeteria, a school can spend $5200 on tables and chairs. Tables cost $200 and chairs cost $40. Each table will have 8 chairs around it. How many tables and chairs will the school purchase?
10 tables and 80 chairs

4. PRICES At a store, toothbrushes cost x dollars and bars of soap cost y dollars. One customer bought 2 toothbrushes and 1 bar of soap for $11. Another customer bought 6 toothbrushes and 5 bars of soap for $38. Both amounts do not include tax. Write and solve a system of equations for x and y.
**$2x + y = 11$
$6x + 5y = 38$
$x = 4.25$ and $y = 2.50$**

GAMES For Exercises 5–7, use the following information.
Mark and Stephanie are playing a game where they toss a dart at a game board that is hanging on the wall. The points earned from a toss depends on where the dart lands. The center area is worth more points than the surrounding area. Each player tosses 12 darts.

5. Stephanie earned a total of 66 points with 6 darts landing in each area. Mark earned a total of 56 points with 4 darts landing in the center area, and 8 darts landing in the surrounding area. Write a system of equations that represents the number of darts each player tossed into each section. Use x for the inner circle, and y for the outer circle.
$6x + 6y = 66$; $4x + 8y = 56$

6. How many points is the inner circle worth? How many points is the outer circle worth?
inner circle = 8 points; outer circle = 3 points

7. If a player gets 10 darts in the inner circle and 2 in the outer circle the total score is doubled. How many points would the player earn if he or she gets exactly 10 darts in the center?
172 points

3-2 Enrichment

Using Coordinates

From one observation point, the line of sight to a downed plane is given by $y = x - 1$. This equation describes the distance from the observation point to the plane in a straight line. From another observation point, the line of sight is given by $x + 3y = 21$. What are the coordinates of the point at which the crash occurred?

Solve the system of equations $\begin{cases} y = x - 1 \\ x + 3y = 21 \end{cases}$.

$x + 3y = 21$
$x + 3(x - 1) = 21$ Substitute $x - 1$ for y.
$x + 3x - 3 = 21$
$4x = 24$
$x = 6$

$x + 3y = 21$
$6 + 3y = 21$ Substitute 6 for x.
$3y = 15$
$y = 5$

The coordinates of the crash are (6, 5).

Solve.

1. The lines of sight to a forest fire are as follows.
From Ranger Station A: $3x + y = 9$
From Ranger Station B: $2x + 3y = 13$
Find the coordinates of the fire.
(2, 3)

2. An airplane is traveling along the line $x - y = -1$ when it sees another airplane traveling along the line $5x + 3y = 19$. If they continue along the same lines, at what point will their flight paths cross?
(2, 3)

3. Two mine shafts are dug along the paths of the following equations.
$x - y = 1400$
$2x + y = 1300$
If the shafts meet at a depth of 200 feet, what are the coordinates of the point at which they meet?
(900, −500)

NAME _____ DATE _____ PERIOD _____

3-3 Study Guide and Intervention

Solving Systems of Inequalities by Graphing

Graph Systems of Inequalities To solve a system of inequalities, graph the inequalities in the same coordinate plane. The solution set is represented by the intersection of the graphs.

Example **Solve the system of inequalities by graphing.**

$y \le 2x - 1$ and $y > \dfrac{x}{3} + 2$

The solution of $y \le 2x - 1$ is Regions 1 and 2.

The solution of $y > \dfrac{x}{3} + 2$ is Regions 1 and 3.

The intersection of these regions is Region 1, which is the solution set of the system of inequalities.

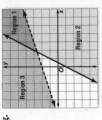

Exercises

Solve each system of inequalities by graphing.

1. $x - y \le 2$
$x + 2y \ge 1$

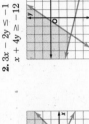

2. $3x - 2y \le -1$
$x + 4y \ge -12$

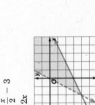

3. $|y| \le 1$
$x > 2$

4. $y \ge \dfrac{x}{2} - 3$
$y < 2x$

5. $y < \dfrac{x}{3} + 2$
$y < -2x + 1$

6. $y \ge -\dfrac{x}{4} + 1$
$y < 3x - 1$

7. $x + y \ge 4$
$2x - y > 2$

8. $x + 3y < 3$
$x - 2y \ge 4$

9. $x - 2y > 6$
$x + 4y < -4$

Chapter 3   21   Glencoe Algebra 2

NAME _____ DATE _____ PERIOD _____

3-3 Lesson Reading Guide

Solving Systems of Inequalities by Graphing

Get Ready for the Lesson

Read the introduction to Lesson 3-3 in your textbook.

Satish is 37 years old. He has a blood pressure reading of 135/99. Is his blood pressure within the normal range? Explain.

Sample answer: No; his systolic pressure is normal, but his diastolic pressure is too high. It should be between 60 and 90.

Read the Lesson

1. Without actually drawing the graph, describe the boundary lines for the system of inequalities shown at the right.

$|x| < 3$
$|y| \le 5$

Two dashed vertical lines ($x = 3$ and $x = -3$) and two solid horizontal lines ($y = -5$ and $y = 5$)

2. Think about how the graph would look for the system given above. What will be the shape of the shaded region? (It is not necessary to draw the graph. See if you can imagine it without drawing anything. If this is difficult to do, make a rough sketch to help you answer the question.)

a rectangle

3. Which system of inequalities matches the graph shown at the right? **B**

A. $x - y \le -2$
$x - y > 2$

B. $x - y \ge -2$
$x - y < 2$

C. $x + y \le -2$
$x + y > 2$

D. $x - y > -2$
$x - y \le 2$

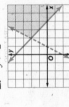

Remember What You Learned

4. To graph a system of inequalities, you must graph two or more boundary lines. When you graph each of these lines, how can the inequality symbols help you remember whether to use a dashed or solid line?

Use a dashed line if the inequality symbol is > or <, because these symbols do not include equality and the dashed line reminds you that the line itself is not included in the graph. Use a solid line if the symbol is ≥ or ≤, because these symbols include equality and tell you that the line itself is included in the graph.

Chapter 3   20   Glencoe Algebra 2

Answers (Lesson 3-3)

Left page (Study Guide and Intervention)

3-3 Study Guide and Intervention (continued)

Solving Systems of Inequalities by Graphing

Find Vertices of a Polygonal Region Sometimes the graph of a system of inequalities forms a bounded region. You can find the vertices of the region by a combination of the methods used earlier in this chapter: graphing, substitution, and/or elimination.

Example **Find the coordinates of the vertices of the figure formed by**
$5x + 4y < 20$, $y < 2x + 3$, and $x - 3y < 4$.

Graph the boundary of each inequality. The intersections of the boundary lines are the vertices of a triangle.

The vertex $(4, 0)$ can be determined from the graph. To find the coordinates of the second and third vertices, solve the two systems of equations

$$y = 2x + 3 \quad \text{and} \quad y = 2x + 3$$
$$5x + 4y = 20 \qquad\qquad x - 3y = 4$$

For the first system of equations, rewrite the first equation in standard form as $2x - y = -3$. Then multiply that equation by 4 and add to the second equation.

$$2x - y = -3 \quad \text{Multiply by 4.} \quad 8x - 4y = -12$$
$$5x + 4y = 20 \qquad\qquad\quad (+)\ 5x + 4y = 20$$
$$\overline{\qquad\qquad\qquad\qquad\qquad 13x \qquad = 8}$$
$$x \qquad = \frac{8}{13}$$

Then substitute $x = \frac{8}{13}$ in one of the original equations and solve for y.

$$2\left(\frac{8}{13}\right) - y = -3$$
$$\frac{16}{13} - y = -3$$
$$y = \frac{55}{13}$$

The coordinates of the second vertex are $\left(\frac{8}{13}, 4\frac{3}{13}\right)$.

For the second system of equations, use substitution. Substitute $2x + 3$ for y in the second equation to get

$$x - 3(2x + 3) = 4$$
$$x - 6x - 9 = 4$$
$$-5x = 13$$
$$x = -\frac{13}{5}$$

Then substitute $x = -\frac{13}{5}$ in the first equation to solve for y.

$$y = 2\left(-\frac{13}{5}\right) + 3$$
$$y = -\frac{26}{5} + 3$$
$$y = -\frac{11}{5}$$

The coordinates of the third vertex are $\left(-2\frac{3}{5}, -2\frac{1}{5}\right)$.

Thus, the coordinates of the three vertices are $(4, 0)$, $\left(\frac{8}{13}, 4\frac{3}{13}\right)$, and $\left(-2\frac{3}{5}, -2\frac{1}{5}\right)$.

Exercises

Find the coordinates of the vertices of the figure formed by each system of inequalities.

1. $y \le -3x + 7$
$y < \frac{1}{2}x + 3$
$y > -2$

(2, 1), (-4, -2),
(3, -2)

2. $x > -3$
$y < -\frac{1}{3}x + 3$
$y > x - 1$

(-3, 4), (3, 2),
(-3, -4)

3. $y < -\frac{1}{2}x + 3$
$y > \frac{1}{2}x + 1$
$y < 3x + 10$

(-2, 4), (2, 2),
$\left(-3\frac{3}{5}, -\frac{4}{5}\right)$

22

Right page (Skills Practice)

3-3 Skills Practice

Solving Systems of Inequalities by Graphing

Solve each system of inequalities by graphing.

1. $x < 1$
$y \ge -1$

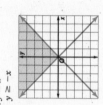

2. $x \ge -3$
$y \ge -3$

3. $x \le 2$
$x > 4$ no solution

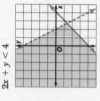

4. $y \ge x$
$y \ge -x$

5. $y < -4x$
$y \ge 3x - 2$

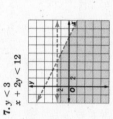

6. $x - y \ge -1$
$3x - y \ge 4$

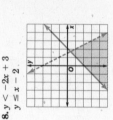

7. $y < 3$
$x + 2y < 12$

8. $y < -2x + 3$
$y \le x - 2$

9. $x - y \le 4$
$2x + y < 4$

Find the coordinates of the vertices of the figure formed by each system of inequalities.

10. $y < 0$
$x < 0$
$y \ge -x - 1$

$(0, 0), (0, -1), (-1, 0)$

11. $y < 3 - x$
$y \ge 3$
$x > -5$

$(0, 3), (-5, 3), (-5, 8)$

12. $x \ge -2$
$y > x - 2$
$x + y \le 2$

$(-2, 4), (2, 2),$
$(-2, -4), (2, 0)$

23

3-3 Practice

NAME _____ DATE _____ PERIOD _____

Solving Systems of Inequalities by Graphing

Solve each system of inequalities by graphing.

1. $y + 1 < -x$
$y \geq 1$

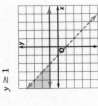

2. $x > -2$
$2y \geq 3x + 6$

3. $y \leq 2x - 3$
$y \leq -\frac{1}{2}x + 2$

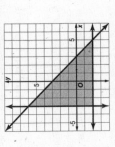

4. $x + y > -2$
$3x - 3y \geq -2$

5. $|y| \leq 1$
$y < x - 1$

6. $3y > 4x$
$2x - 3y > -6$

Find the coordinates of the vertices of the figure formed by each system of inequalities.

7. $y \geq 1 - x$
$y \leq x - 1$
$x \leq 3$

$(1, 0), (3, 2), (3, -2)$

8. $x - y \geq 2$
$x + y \leq 2$
$x \geq -2$

$(-2, 4), (-2, -4), (2, 0)$

9. $y \geq 2x - 2$
$2x + 3y \geq 6$
$y < 4$

$(-3, 4), (-2, -4), \left(\frac{3}{2}, 1\right), (3, 4)$

DRAMA For Exercises 10 and 11, use the following information.

The drama club is selling tickets to its play. An adult ticket costs $15 and a student ticket costs $11. The auditorium will seat 300 ticket-holders. The drama club wants to collect at least $3630 from ticket sales.

10. Write and graph a system of four inequalities that describe how many of each type of ticket the club must sell to meets its goal.

$x \geq 0, y \geq 0, x + y \leq 300, 15x + 11y \geq 3630$

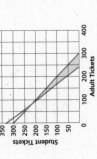

Play Tickets

11. List three different combinations of tickets sold that satisfy the inequalities. **Sample answer:** 250 adult and 50 student, 200 adult and 100 student, 145 adult and 148 student

---

3-3 Word Problem Practice

NAME _____ DATE _____ PERIOD _____

Solving Systems of Inequalities by Graphing

1. BIRD BATH Melissa wants to put a bird bath in her yard at point (x, y), and wants it to be is inside the enclosed shaded area shown in the graph.

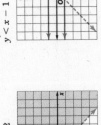

First, she checks that $x \geq -3$ and $y \geq -2$. What linear inequality must she check to conclude that (x, y) is inside the triangle?

$x + y \leq 3$

2. SQUARES Matt finds a blot of ink covering his writing in his notes for math class. He sees "A square is defined by $|x| \leq 8$ and __." Write an inequality that completes this sentence.

A square is defined by
$|x|, 8 \text{ an}$

Sample answer: $|y| \leq 8$.

3. HOLIDAY Amanda received presents and cards from friends over the holiday season. Every present came with one card and none of her friends sent her more than one card. Less than 10 of her friends sent only a card. Describe this situation using inequalities.
Let p be the number of presents and c be the number of cards.

$p \leq c$ and $c - p < 10$

4. DECK The Wrights are building a deck. The deck is defined by the inequalities $x \leq 5$, $0.25x + y \geq -4.75$, $y \leq 5$, and $4.5x + y \geq -17.5$. Graph the inequalities and find the coordinates of the deck's corners.

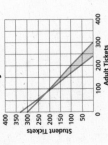

$(5, 5), (-5, 5), (5, -6), (-3, -4)$

TICKETS For Exercises 5 and 6, use the following information.

A theater charges $10 for adults and $5 for children 12 or under. The theater makes a profit if they can sell more than $600 worth of tickets. The theater has seating for 100 people.

5. Write a system of linear inequalities that describes the situation.
Let A be the number of adults and C be the number of children:

$A \geq 0$, $C \geq 0$, $A + C \leq 100$,
$10A + 5C \geq 600$.

6. Graph the solution to the inequalities. Can the theater make a profit if no adults come to the performance?

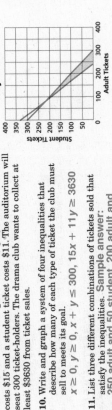

no

3-3 Enrichment

NAME _____ DATE _____ PERIOD _____

Creative Designs

A system of linear inequalities can be used to define the region bounded by a geometric shape graphed on a coordinate plane. For example, the rectangle shown can be defined by the system

$x \leq 4$
$x \geq 0$
$y \leq 3$
$y \geq 0.$

The triangle shown can be described using the inequalities

$x + 2y \leq 4$
$x \geq 0$
$y \geq 1.$

1. Find a system of linear inequalities to describe the area bounded by the bow tie shape below. The intersection points are (1, 1), (1, 4), (3, 3), (5, 2), and (5, 5).

$$\textit{If } 1 \leq x \leq 3 \quad \textit{if } 3 \leq x \leq 5$$
$$y \geq x \qquad\quad y \leq x$$
$$x + 2y \geq 9 \qquad x + 2y \geq 9$$

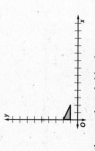

2. Find a system of linear inequalities to describe the area bounded by the basic 'house' shape shown below. The intersection points are (1,1), (1,5), (3,7), (5,5), and (5,1).

$x \geq 1$
$x \leq 5$
$y \leq x + 4$
$y \geq -x + 10$
$y \geq 1$

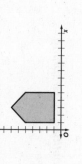

Chapter 3   26   Glencoe Algebra 2

3-4 Lesson Reading Guide

Linear Programming

NAME _____ DATE _____ PERIOD _____

Get Ready for the Lesson

Read the introduction to Lesson 3-4 in your textbook.

Name two or more facts that indicate that you will need to use inequalities to model this situation.

Sample answer: The buoy tender can carry up to 8 new buoys. There seems to be a limit of 24 hours on the time the crew has at sea. The crew will want to repair or replace the maximum number of buoys possible.

Read the Lesson

1. Complete each sentence.

   a. When you find the feasible region for a linear programming problem, you are solving a system of linear **inequalities** called **constraints**. The points in the feasible region are **solutions** of the system.

   b. The corner points of a polygonal region are the **vertices** of the feasible region.

2. A polygonal region always takes up only a limited part of the coordinate plane. One way to think of this is to imagine a circle or rectangle that the region would fit inside. In the case of a polygonal region, you can always find a circle or rectangle that is large enough to contain all the points of the polygonal region. What word is used to describe a region that can be enclosed in this way? What word is used to describe a region that is too large to be enclosed in this way? **bounded; unbounded**

3. How do you find the corner points of the polygonal region in a linear programming problem? **You solve a system of two linear equations.**

4. What are some everyday meanings of the word *feasible* that remind you of the mathematical meaning of the term *feasible region*?
   Sample answer: possible or achievable

Remember What You Learned

5. Look up the word *constraint* in a dictionary. If more than one definition is given, choose the one that seems closest to the idea of a *constraint* in a linear programming problem. How can this definition help you to remember the meaning of *constraint* as it is used in this lesson? **Sample answer:** A *constraint* is a restriction or limitation. The constraints in a linear programming problem are restrictions on the variables that translate into inequality statements.

Chapter 3   27   Glencoe Algebra 2

NAME _____ DATE _____ PERIOD _____

3-4 Study Guide and Intervention (continued)

Linear Programming

Real-World Problems When solving linear programming problems, use the following procedure.

1. Define variables.
2. Write a system of inequalities.
3. Graph the system of inequalities.
4. Find the coordinates of the vertices of the feasible region.
5. Write an expression to be maximized or minimized.
6. Substitute the coordinates of the vertices in the expression.
7. Select the greatest or least result to answer the problem.

Example A painter has exactly 32 units of yellow dye and 54 units of green dye. He plans to mix as many gallons as possible of color A and color B. Each gallon of color A requires 4 units of yellow dye and 1 unit of green dye. Each gallon of color B requires 1 unit of yellow dye and 6 units of green dye. Find the maximum number of gallons he can mix.

Step 1 Define the variables.
x = the number of gallons of color A made
y = the number of gallons of color B made

Step 2 Write a system of inequalities.
Since the number of gallons made cannot be negative, $x \geq 0$ and $y \geq 0$.
There are 32 units of yellow dye; each gallon of color A requires 4 units, and each gallon of color B requires 1 unit.
So $4x + y \leq 32$.
Similarly for the green dye, $x + 6y \leq 54$.

Steps 3 and 4 Graph the system of inequalities and find the coordinates of the vertices of the feasible region. The vertices of the feasible region are (0, 0), (0, 9), (6, 8), and (8, 0).

Steps 5-7 Find the maximum number of gallons, $x + y$, that he can make. The maximum number of gallons the painter can make is 14, 6 gallons of color A and 8 gallons of color B.

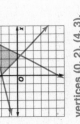
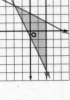
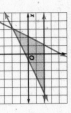

Exercises

1. **FOOD** A delicatessen has 12 pounds of plain sausage and 10 pounds of spicy sausage. A pound of Bratwurst A contains $\frac{3}{4}$ pound of plain sausage and $\frac{1}{4}$ pound of spicy sausage. A pound of Bratwurst B contains $\frac{1}{2}$ pound of each sausage. Find the maximum number of pounds of bratwurst that can be made.
4 pounds of Bratwurst A and 18 pounds of Bratwurst B

2. **MANUFACTURING** Machine A can produce 30 steering wheels per hour at a cost of $8 per hour. Machine B can produce 40 steering wheels per hour at a cost of $12 per hour. The company can use either machine by itself or both machines at the same time. What is the minimum number of hours needed to produce 380 steering wheels if the cost must be no more than $108? **6 hours; 6 hours on Machine A and 5 hours on Machine B simultaneously**

Chapter 3   29   *Glencoe Algebra 2*

NAME _____ DATE _____ PERIOD _____

3-4 Study Guide and Intervention

Linear Programming

Maximum and Minimum Values When a system of linear inequalities produces a bounded polygonal region, the *maximum* or *minimum* value of a related function will occur at a vertex of the region.

Example Graph the system of inequalities. Name the coordinates of the vertices or the feasible region. Find the maximum and minimum values of the function $f(x, y) = 3x + 2y$ for this polygonal region.

$y \leq 4$
$y \leq -x + 6$
$y \geq \frac{1}{2}x - \frac{3}{2}$
$y \geq 6x + 4$

First find the vertices of the bounded region. Graph the inequalities.

The polygon formed is a quadrilateral with vertices at (0, 4), (2, 4), (5, 1), and (-1, -2). Use the table to find the maximum and minimum values of $f(x, y) = 3x + 2y$.

(x, y)	$3x + 2y$	$f(x, y)$
(0, 4)	3(0) + 2(4)	8
(2, 4)	3(2) + 2(4)	14
(5, 1)	3(5) + 2(1)	17
(-1, -2)	3(-1) + 2(-2)	-7

The maximum value is 17 at (5, 1). The minimum value is -7 at (-1, -2).

Exercises

Graph each system of inequalities. Name the coordinates of the vertices of the feasible region. Find the maximum and minimum values of the given function for this region.

1. $y \geq 2$
$1 \leq x \leq 5$
$y \leq x + 3$
$f(x, y) = 3x - 2y$

vertices: (1, 2), (1, 4), (5, 8), (5, 2); max: 11; min: -5

2. $y \geq -2$
$y \geq 2x - 4$
$x - 2y \geq -1$
$f(x, y) = 4x - y$

vertices: (-5, -2), (3, 2), (1, -2); max: 10; min: -18

3. $x + y \geq 2$
$4y \leq x + 8$
$y \geq 2x - 5$
$f(x, y) = 4x + 3y$

vertices: (0, 2), (4, 3), $\left(\frac{7}{3}, -\frac{1}{3}\right)$; max: 25; min: 6

Chapter 3   28   *Glencoe Algebra 2*

Answers (Lesson 3-4)

3-4 Practice

Linear Programming

Graph each system of inequalities. Name the coordinates of the vertices of the feasible region. Find the maximum and minimum values of the given function for this region.

1. $2x - 4 \le y$
$-2x - 4 \le y$
$y \le 2$
$f(x, y) = -2x + y$

max.: 8, min.: −4

2. $3x - y \le 7$
$2x - y \ge 3$
$y \ge x - 3$
$f(x, y) = x - 4y$

max.: 12, min.: −16

3. $x \ge 0$
$y \ge 0$
$y \le 6$
$y \le -3x + 15$
$f(x, y) = 3x + y$

max.: 15, min.: 0

4. $x \le 0$
$y \le 0$
$4x + y \ge -7$
$f(x, y) = -x - 4y$

max.: 28, min.: 0

5. $y \le 3x + 6$
$4y + 3x \le 3$
$x \ge -2$
$f(x, y) = -x + 3y$

max.: $\dfrac{34}{5}$, no min.

6. $2x + 3y \ge 6$
$2x - y \ge 2$
$x \ge 0$
$y \ge 0$
$f(x, y) = x + 4y + 3$

no max., min.: $\dfrac{17}{2}$

PRODUCTION For Exercises 7–9, use the following information.
A glass blower can form 8 simple vases or 2 elaborate vases in an hour. In a work shift of no more than 8 hours, the worker must form at least 40 vases.

7. Let *s* represent the hours forming simple vases and *e* the hours forming elaborate vases. Write a system of inequalities involving the time spent on each type of vase.
$s \ge 0, e \ge 0, s + e \le 8, 8s + 2e \ge 40$

8. If the glass blower makes a profit of $30 per hour worked on the simple vases and $35 per hour worked on the elaborate vases, write a function for the total profit on the vases.
$f(s, e) = 30s + 35e$

9. Find the number of hours the worker should spend on each type of vase to maximize profit. What is that profit? 4 h on each; $260

3-4 Skills Practice

Linear Programming

Graph each system of inequalities. Name the coordinates of the vertices of the feasible region. Find the maximum and minimum values of the given function for this region.

1. $x \ge 2$
$x \le 5$
$y \ge 1$
$y \le 4$
$f(x, y) = x + y$

max.: 9, min.: 3

2. $x \ge 1$
$y \ge 6$
$y \ge x - 2$
$f(x, y) = x - y$

max.: 2, min.: −5

3. $x \ge 0$
$y \ge 0$
$y \le 7 - x$
$f(x, y) = 3x + y$

max.: 21, min.: 0

4. $x \ge -1$
$x + y \le 6$
$f(x, y) = x + 2y$

max.: 13, no min.

5. $y \le 2x$
$y \le 6 - x$
$y \le 6$
$f(x, y) = 4x + 3y$

no max., min.: 20

6. $y \ge -x - 2$
$y \le 3x + 2$
$y \le x + 4$
$f(x, y) = -3x + 5y$

max.: 22, min.: −2

7. MANUFACTURING A backpack manufacturer produces an internal frame pack and an external frame pack. Let *x* represent the number of internal frame packs produced in one hour and let *y* represent the number of external frame packs produced in one hour. Then the inequalities $x + 3y \le 18$, $2x + y \le 16$, $x \ge 0$, and $y \ge 0$ describe the constraints for manufacturing both packs. Use the profit function $f(x) = 50x + 80y$ and the constraints given to determine the maximum profit for manufacturing both backpacks for the given constraints. $620

NAME _____ DATE _____ PERIOD _____

3-4 Enrichment

Sensitivity Analysis

A linear programming model has specific objective coefficients. For example, if the value of a model is found by $2x + 3y = 5$, the objective coefficients are (2, 3). What if these coefficients were (2.1, 2.9) or (2.5, 3.1)? How would these changes affect the optimal linear program value? This type of investigation is called **sensitivity analysis**.

In general, the objective function in two-variable linear programming problem can be written as: maximize (or minimize) $Ax + By = C$, subject to a set of constraint equations. Changes to the *parameters A and B* could change the slope of the line. This change of slope could lead to a change in the optimum solution to a different corner point (Recall, the optimum solution occurs at a *corner point*).

There is a range in the slope value that will produce this change, thus there is a range of variation for both A and B that will keep the optimal solution the same (see graph).

1. Find the slope of $Ax + By = C$ and observe how changes to the parameters A and B can change the slope of the line.
The slope, m, of $Ax + By = C$ is $m = -\dfrac{A}{B}$.

Consider the Linear Programming problem:

Maximize: $\quad C = 2x + 3y,$
Subject to: $\quad 3x + y \le 21$
$\qquad\qquad x + y \le 9$
$\qquad\qquad y \le x$
$\qquad\qquad y \le 4$

(x, y)	$(0, 0)$	$(4, 4)$	$(5, 4)$	$(6, 3)$	$(7, 0)$
C	0	20	22	21	14

After finding the intersections and evaluating the objective equation, we find the maximal solution is (5, 4). If the objective coefficients are changed from 2 and 3 to A and B, the optimum solution with remain at (5, 4) while the slope remains between the slope of $x + y \le 9$ and the slope of $3x + y \le 21$. If not, then the new optimal solution will be at (4, 4) or (6, 3).

2. Express the relationship, the slope of the objective function is between the slope of the line $x + y = 9$ and the slope of the line $3x + y = 21$, algebraically.
$$-3 \le \dfrac{A}{B} \le -1$$

3. Determine the range on A if B remains equal to 3.
$$-9 \le A \le -3$$

NAME _____ DATE _____ PERIOD _____

3-4 Word Problem Practice

Linear Programming

1. **REGIONS** A region in the plane is formed by the equations $x - y < 3$, $x - y > -3$, and $x + y > -3$. Is this region bounded or unbounded? Explain.
The region is unbounded because it is open. The points (n, n) are in the region for all positive values of n.

2. **MANUFACTURING** Eighty workers are available to assemble tables and chairs. It takes 5 people to assemble a table and 3 people to assemble a chair. The workers always make at least as many tables as chairs because the tables are easier to make. If x is the number of tables and y is the number of chairs, the system of inequalities that represent what can be assembled is $x > 0, y > 0$, $y \le x$, and $5x + 3y \le 80$. What is the maximum total number of chairs and tables the workers can make?
10 tables and 10 chairs

3. **FISH** An aquarium is 2000 cubic inches. Nathan wants to populate the aquarium with neon tetras and catfish. It is recommended that each neon tetra be allowed 50 cubic inches and each catfish be allowed 200 cubic inches of space. Nathan would like at least one catfish for every 4 neon tetras. Let n be the number of neon tetra and c be the number of catfish. The following inequalities form the feasible region for this situation: $n > 0, c > 0, 4c \ge n$, and $50n + 200c \le 2000$. What is the maximum number of fish Nathan can put in his aquarium?
$20 + 5 = 25$

4. **ELEVATION** A trapezoidal park is built on a slight incline. The function for the ground elevation above sea level is $f(x, y) = x - 3y + 20$ feet. What are the coordinates of the highest point in the park?

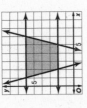

(5, 2)

5. **CERAMICS** For Exercises 5–7, use the following information.
Josh has 8 days to make pots and plates to sell at a local fair. Each pot weighs 2 pounds and each plate weighs 1 pound. Josh cannot carry more than 50 pounds to the fair. Each day, he can make at most 5 plates and at most 3 pots. He will make $12 profit for every plate and $25 profit for every pot that he sells.

5. Write linear inequalities to represent the number of pots p and plates a Josh may bring to the fair.
$a \ge 0, p \ge 0, 2p + a \le 50, a \le 40,$ and $p \le 24.$

6. List the coordinates of the vertices of the feasible region.
$(0, 0), (0, 24), (40, 0), (2, 24),$ $(40, 5)$ where the horizontal axis is taken to represent a

7. How many pots and how many plates should Josh make to maximize his potential profit?
2 plates and 24 pots

3-5 Lesson Reading Guide

NAME _____ DATE _____ PERIOD _____

Solving Systems of Equations in Three Variables

Get Ready for the Lesson

Read the introduction to Lesson 3-5 in your textbook.

At the 1960 Summer Olympics in Rome, Italy, the United States won 71 medals. The U.S. team won 13 more gold medals than silver and 5 fewer bronze medals than silver. Using the same variables as those in the introduction, write a system of equations that describes the medals won for the 1960 Olympics.

$g + s + b = 71; g = s + 13; b = s - 5$

Read the Lesson

1. The planes for the equations in a system of three linear equations in three variables determine the number of solutions. Match each graph description below with the description of the number of solutions of the system. (Some of the items on the right may be used more than once, and not all possible types of graphs are listed.)

   a. three parallel planes ___**II**___   **I.** one solution

   b. three planes that intersect in a line ___**III**___   **II.** no solutions

   c. three planes that intersect in one point ___**I**___   **III.** infinite solutions

   d. one plane that represents all three equations ___**III**___

2. Suppose that three classmates, Monique, Josh, and Lilly, are studying for a quiz on this lesson. They work together on solving a system of equations in three variables, x, y, and z, following the algebraic method shown in your textbook. They first find that $z = 3$, then that $y = -2$, and finally that $x = -1$. The students agree on these values, but disagree on how to write the solution. Here are their answers:

   Monique: $(3, -2, -1)$ Josh: $(-2, -1, 3)$ Lilly: $(-1, -2, 3)$

   a. How do you think each student decided on the order of the numbers in the ordered triple? **Sample answer: Monique arranged the values in the order in which she found them. Josh arranged them from smallest to largest. Lilly arranged them in alphabetical order of the variables.**

   b. Which student is correct? **Lilly**

Remember What You Learned

3. How can you remember that obtaining the equation $0 = 0$ indicates a system with infinitely many solutions, while obtaining an equation such as $0 = 8$ indicates a system with no solutions? $0 = 0$ is always true, while $0 = 8$ is never true.

Chapter 3   35   *Glencoe Algebra 2*

3-4 Graphing Calculator Activity

NAME _____ DATE _____ PERIOD _____

Linear Programming

A graphing calculator can store the x- and y-coordinates when using the **intersect** command in the [CALC] menu. This can be displayed on the home screen and used to evaluate an expression with x and y variables. This process is useful in finding the vertices of the feasible region and determining the maximum or minimum value for $f(x, y)$.

Example   Graph the system $x - 3y \geq -7$, $5x + y \leq 13$, $x + 6y \geq -9$, $3x - 2y \geq -7$, and $f(x, y) = 4x - 3y$. Find the coordinates of the feasible region. Then find the maximum and minimum values for the system.

Solve each inequality for y. Enter each boundary equation in the **Y=** screen. Find the vertices of the feasible region. Then find the values of $f(x, y)$ to determine the maximum and minimum values.

Keystrokes: Y= (1 + 3) X,T,θ,n + 7 3) ENTER
(-) 5 X,T,θ,n + 13 ENTER (-) (1 + 6) X,T,θ,n + 3 +
2) ÷ 2 ENTER 3 ÷ 2 X,T,θ,n + 7 ÷ 2) ZOOM 6

2nd [CALC] 5 ENTER ENTER ENTER 2nd [QUIT] 2nd [[ ]
X,T,θ,n . [CALC] 5 ▸ 4 X,T,θ,n − 3 ALPHA [Y] 2nd [ ]] ENTER
GRAPH 2nd [CALC] 5 ▸ [CALC] 5 ▸ ENTER 2nd [QUIT]
2nd [ENTRY] ENTER ENTER [CALC] 5 ▸ ▸ GRAPH 2nd
ENTER ENTER 2nd [QUIT] 2nd [ENTRY] ENTER GRAPH 2nd
[CALC] 5 ENTER ▸ ◂ ENTER ENTER 2nd [QUIT]
[ENTRY] ENTER.

$(x, y, 4x-3y) = (2 3 -13)$
$(x, y, 4x-3y) = (-2 18)$
$(x, y, 4x-3y) = (-1 -9)$
$(x, y, 4x-3y) = (-1 2 -10)$

[-10, 10] scl:1 by [-10, 10] scl:1

The maximum value of the system is 18 and the minimum value is -10.

Exercises

Graph each system. Find the coordinates of the vertices of the feasible region. Then find the maximum and minimum values for the system.

1. $2x + 3y \geq 6$
   $3x - 2y \geq -4$
   $5x + y \geq 15$
   $f(x, y) = x + 3y$

[-10, 10] scl:1 by [-10, 10] scl:1
$(0, 2), (3, 0), (2, 5)$;
min. = 3, max. = 17

2. $y \leq 4x + 6$
   $x + 4y \leq 7$
   $2x + y \geq 7$
   $x - 6y \leq 10$
   $f(x, y) = 2x - y$

[-10, 10] scl:1 by [-10, 10] scl:1
$(-1, 2), (-2, -2), (3, 1)$,
$(4, -1)$; min. = -4, max. = 9

3. $y \leq 16 - x$
   $0 \leq 2y \leq 17$
   $2x + 3y \geq 11$
   $y \leq 3x + 1$
   $y \geq 2x - 13$
   $y \geq 7 - 2x$
   $f(x, y) = 5x + 6y$

[-10, 10] scl:1 by [-10, 10] scl:1
$(5.5, 0), (6.5, 0), (7.5, 8.5)$,
$(1.2, 4.6), (2.5, 2), (9.66, 6.33)$;
min. = 24.5, max. = 88.5

Chapter 3   34   *Glencoe Algebra 2*

Left Page (36)

NAME _____ DATE _____ PERIOD _____

3-5 Study Guide and Intervention

Solving Systems of Equations in Three Variables

Systems in Three Variables Use the methods used for solving systems of linear equations in two variables to solve systems of equations in three variables. A system of three equations in three variables can have a unique solution, infinitely many solutions, or no solution. A solution is an ordered triple.

Example Solve this system of equations.

$$3x + y - z = -6$$
$$2x - y + 2z = 8$$
$$4x + y - 3z = -21$$

Step 1 Use elimination to make a system of two equations in two variables.

$$\begin{array}{ll} 3x + y - z = -6 & \text{First equation} \\ (+)\ 2x - y + 2z = 8 & \text{Second equation} \\ \hline 5x + z = 2 & \text{Add to eliminate } y. \end{array}$$

$$\begin{array}{ll} 2x - y + 2z = 8 & \text{Second equation} \\ (+)\ 4x + y - 3z = -21 & \text{Third equation} \\ \hline 6x - z = -13 & \text{Add to eliminate } y. \end{array}$$

Step 2 Solve the system of two equations.

$$\begin{array}{ll} 5x + z = 2 & \\ (+)\ 6x - z = -13 & \\ \hline 11x = -11 & \text{Add to eliminate } z. \\ x = -1 & \text{Divide both sides by 11.} \end{array}$$

Substitute -1 for x in one of the equations with two variables and solve for z.

$$\begin{array}{ll} 5x + z = 2 & \text{Equation with two variables} \\ 5(-1) + z = 2 & \text{Replace } x \text{ with } -1. \\ -5 + z = 2 & \text{Multiply.} \\ z = 7 & \text{Add 5 to both sides.} \end{array}$$

The result so far is $x = -1$ and $z = 7$.

Step 3 Substitute -1 for x and 7 for z in one of the original equations with three variables.

$$\begin{array}{ll} 3x + y - z = -6 & \text{Original equation with three variables} \\ 3(-1) + y - 7 = -6 & \text{Replace } x \text{ with } -1 \text{ and } z \text{ with 7.} \\ -3 + y - 7 = -6 & \text{Multiply.} \\ y = 4 & \text{Simplify.} \end{array}$$

The solution is $(-1, 4, 7)$.

Exercises

Solve each system of equations.

1. $2x + 3y - z = 0$
$x - 2y - 4z = 14$
$3x + y - 8z = 17$
$(4, -3, -1)$

2. $2x - y + 4z = 11$
$x + 2y - 6z = -11$
$3x - y - 10z = 11$
$\left(2, -5, \dfrac{1}{2}\right)$

3. $x - 2y + z = 8$
$2x + y - z = 0$
$3x - 6y + 3z = 24$
infinitely many solutions

4. $3x - y - z = 5$
$3x + 2y - z = 11$
$6x - 3y + 2z = -12$
$\left(\dfrac{2}{3}, 2, -5\right)$

5. $2x - 4y - z = 10$
$4x - 8y - 2z = 16$
$3x + y + z = 12$
no solution

6. $x - 6y + 4z = 2$
$2x + 4y - 8z = 16$
$x - 2y = 5$
infinitely many solutions

Right Page (37)

NAME _____ DATE _____ PERIOD _____

3-5 Study Guide and Intervention (continued)

Solving Systems of Equations in Three Variables

Real-World Problems

Example The Laredo Sports Shop sold 10 balls, 3 bats, and 2 bases for $99 on Monday. On Tuesday they sold 4 balls, 8 bats, and 2 bases for $78. On Wednesday they sold 2 balls, 3 bats, and 1 base for $33.60. What are the prices of 1 ball, 1 bat, and 1 base?

First define the variables.

x = price of 1 ball
y = price of 1 bat
z = price of 1 base

Translate the information in the problem into three equations.

$$10x + 3y + 2z = 99$$
$$4x + 8y + 2z = 78$$
$$2x + 3y + z = 33.60$$

Subtract the second equation from the first equation to eliminate z.

$$\begin{array}{l} 10x + 3y + 2z = 99 \\ (-)\ 4x + 8y + 2z = 78 \\ \hline 6x - 5y = 21 \end{array}$$

Multiply the third equation by 2 and subtract from the second equation.

$$\begin{array}{l} 4x + 8y + 2z = 78 \\ (-)\ 4x + 6y + 2z = 67.20 \\ \hline 2y = 10.80 \\ y = 5.40 \end{array}$$

Substitute 5.40 for y in the equation $6x - 5y = 21$.

$$\begin{array}{l} 6x - 5(5.40) = 21 \\ 6x = 48 \\ x = 8 \end{array}$$

Substitute 8 for x and 5.40 for y in one of the original equations to solve for z.

$$\begin{array}{l} 10x + 3y + 2z = 99 \\ 10(8) + 3(5.40) + 2z = 99 \\ 80 + 16.20 + 2z = 99 \\ 2z = 2.80 \\ z = 1.40 \end{array}$$

So a ball costs $8, a bat $5.40, and a base $1.40.

Exercises

1. **FITNESS TRAINING** Carly is training for a triathlon. In her training routine each week, she runs 7 times as far as she swims, and she bikes 3 times as far as she runs. One week she trained a total of 232 miles. How far did she run that week? **56 miles**

2. **ENTERTAINMENT** At the arcade, Ryan, Sara, and Tim played video racing games, pinball, and air hockey. Ryan spent $6 for 6 racing games, 2 pinball games, and 1 game of air hockey. Sara spent $12 for 3 racing games, 4 pinball games, and 5 games of air hockey. Tim spent $12.25 for 2 racing games, 7 pinball games, and 4 games of air hockey. How much did each of the games cost? **racing game: $0.50; pinball: $0.75; air hockey: $1.50**

3. **FOOD** A natural food store makes its own brand of trail mix out of dried apples, raisins, and peanuts. One pound of the mixture costs $3.18. It contains twice as much peanuts by weight as apples. One pound of dried apples costs $4.48, a pound of raisins $2.40, and a pound of peanuts $3.44. How many ounces of each ingredient are contained in 1 pound of the trail mix? **3 oz of apples, 7 oz of raisins, 6 oz of peanuts**

Answers

3-5 Skills Practice

NAME _____ DATE _____ PERIOD _____

Solving Systems of Equations in Three Variables

Solve each system of equations.

1. $2a + c = -10$ $\quad$ **(5, −5, −20)**
   $b - c = 15$
   $a - 2b + c = -5$

2. $x + y + z = 3$ $\quad$ **(0, 2, 1)**
   $13x + 2z = 2$
   $-x - 5z = -5$

3. $2x + 5y + 2z = 6$ $\quad$ **(−3, 2, 1)**
   $5x - 7y = -29$
   $z = 1$

4. $x + 4y - z = 1$ $\quad$ **no solution**
   $3x - y + 8z = 0$
   $x + 4y - z = 10$

5. $-2z = -6$ $\quad$ **(2, −1, 3)**
   $2x + 3y - z = -2$
   $x + 2y + 3z = 9$

6. $3x - 2y + 2z = -2$ $\quad$ **(−2, 1, 3)**
   $x + 6y - 2z = -2$
   $x + 2y = 0$

7. $-x - 5z = -5$ $\quad$ **(0, 0, 1)**
   $y - 3x = 0$
   $13x + 2z = 2$

8. $-3r + 2t = 1$ $\quad$ **(1, −6, 2)**
   $4r + s - 2t = -6$
   $r + s + 4t = 3$

9. $x - y + 3z = 3$ $\quad$ **no solution**
   $-2x + 2y - 6z = 6$
   $y - 5z = -3$

10. $5m + 3n + p = 4$ $\quad$ **(−2, 3, 5)**
    $3m + 2n = 0$
    $2m - n + 3p = 8$

11. $2x + 2y + 2z = -2$ $\quad$ **infinitely many**
    $2x + 3y + 2z = 4$
    $x + y + z = -1$

12. $x + 2y - z = 4$ $\quad$ **(1, 2, 1)**
    $3x - y + 2z = 3$
    $-x + 3y + z = 6$

13. $3x - 2y + z = 1$ $\quad$ **(5, 7, 0)**
    $-x + y - z = 2$
    $5x + 2y + 10z = 39$

14. $3x - 5y + 2z = -12$ $\quad$ **infinitely many**
    $x + 4y - 2z = 8$
    $-3x + 5y - 2z = 12$

15. $2x + y + 3z = -2$ $\quad$ **(−1, 3, −1)**
    $x - y - z = -3$
    $3x - 2y + 3z = -12$

16. $2x - 4y + 3z = 0$ $\quad$ **(3, 0, −2)**
    $x - 2y - 5z = 13$
    $5x + 3y - 2z = 19$

17. $-2x + y + 2z = 2$ $\quad$ **(1, −2, 3)**
    $3x + 3y + z = 0$
    $x + y + z = 2$

18. $x - 2y + 2z = -1$ $\quad$ **infinitely many**
    $x + 2y - z = 6$
    $-3x + 6y - 6z = 3$

19. The sum of three numbers is 18. The sum of the first and second numbers is 15, and the first number is 3 times the third number. Find the numbers. **9, 6, 3**

Chapter 3 — 38 — *Glencoe Algebra 2*

3-5 Practice

NAME _____ DATE _____ PERIOD _____

Solving Systems of Equations in Three Variables

Solve each system of equations.

1. $2x - y + 2z = 15$
   $-x + y + z = 3$
   $3x - y + 2z = 18$
   (3, 1, 5)

2. $x - 4y + 3z = -27$
   $2x + 2y - 3z = 22$
   $4z = -16$
   (1, 4, −4)

3. $a + b = 3$
   $-b + c = 3$
   $a + 2e = 10$
   (2, 1, 4)

4. $3m - 2n + 4p = 15$
   $m - n + p = 3$
   $m + 4n - 5p = 0$
   (3, 3, 3)

5. $2g + 3h - 8j = 10$
   $g - 4h = 1$
   $-2g - 3h + 8j = 5$
   no solution

6. $2x + y - z = -8$
   $4x - y + 2z = -3$
   $-3x + y + 2z = 5$
   (−2, −3, 1)

7. $2x - 5y + z = 5$
   $3x + 2y - z = 17$
   $4x - 3y + 2z = 17$
   (5, 1, 0)

8. $2x + 3y + 4z = 2$
   $5x - 2y + 3z = 0$
   $x - 5y - 2z = -4$
   (2, 2, −2)

9. $p + 4r = -7$
   $p - 3q = -8$
   $q + r = 1$
   (1, 3, −2)

10. $4x + 4y - 2z = 8$
    $3x - 5y + 3z = 0$
    $2x + 2y = 4$
    infinitely many

11. $d + 3e + f = 0$
    $-d + 2e + f = -1$
    $4d + e - f = 1$
    (1, −1, 2)

12. $4x + 4y + 5z = -9$
    $x - 4y - 2z = -2$
    $2x + 3y - 2z = 21$
    (2, 3, −4)

13. $5x + 9y + z = 20$
    $2x - y - z = -21$
    $5x + 2y + 2z = -21$
    (−7, 6, 1)

14. $2x + y - 3z = -3$
    $3x + 2y + 4z = 5$
    $-6x - 3y + 9z = 9$
    infinitely many

15. $3x + 3y + z = 10$
    $5x + 2y + 2z = 7$
    $3x - 2y + 3z = -9$
    (1, 3, −2)

16. $2u + v + w = 2$
    $-3u + 2v + 3w = 7$
    $-u - v + 2w = 7$
    (0, −1, 3)

17. $x + 5y - 3z = -18$
    $3x - 2y + 5z = 22$
    $-2x - 3y + 8z = 28$
    (1, −2, 3)

18. $x - 2y + z = -1$
    $-x + y - z = 6$
    $-4y + 2z = 1$
    no solution

19. $2x - 2y - 4z = -2$
    $3x - 3y - 6z = -3$
    $-2x + 3y + z = 7$
    (4, 5, 0)

20. $x - y + 9z = -27$
    $2x - 4y - z = -1$
    $3x + 6y - 3z = 27$
    (2, 2, −3)

21. $2x - 5y - 3z = 7$
    $-4x + 10y + 2z = 6$
    $6x - 15y - z = -19$
    infinitely many

22. The sum of three numbers is 6. The third number is the sum of the first and second numbers. The first number is one more than the third number. Find the numbers. **4, −1, 3**

23. The sum of three numbers is −4. The second number decreased by the third is equal to the first. The sum of the first and second numbers is −5. Find the numbers. **−3, −2, 1**

24. **SPORTS** Alexandria High School scored 37 points in a football game. Six points are awarded for each touchdown. After each touchdown, the team can earn one point for the extra kick or two points for a 2-point conversion. The team scored one fewer 2-point conversions than extra kicks. The team scored 10 times during the game. How many touchdowns were made during the game? **5**

Chapter 3 — 39 — *Glencoe Algebra 2*

NAME _____ DATE _____ PERIOD _____

3-5 Enrichment

Homogenous Systems

A system of equations is called homogeneous if it is of the form:

$$gx + hy + kz = 0$$
$$bx + ey + fz = 0$$
$$ax + by + cz = 0$$

Homogeneous systems have some unique characteristics that set them apart from general systems of equations. The following exercises will explore some of these unique characteristics.

1. Evaluate the following statement. Is this statement *always*, *sometimes*, or *never* true? Explain your reasoning.
Every homogeneous system of equations will have at least one trivial solution: (0, 0, 0).
Always; Sample answer: if you replace each variable with 0, you will always get each equation equal to 0.

2. Find a non-trivial solution to the following homogenous system of equations.

$$x + y + 5z = 0$$
$$2x + y + 7z = 0$$
$$x + 2z = 0$$

$x = -2z$ and $y = -3z$; Choose a number for z, for example, $z = 1$. So, a sample answer is $(-2, -3, 1)$.

3. Multiply the solution you found in Exercise 2 by 3. Is the new ordered triple a solution to the system?
yes

4. Multiply the solution you found in Exercise 2 by -6. Is the new ordered triple a solution to the system?
yes

5. Make a conjecture about any multiple of a given solution to a homogeneous system of equations.
Sample answer: any multiple of a given solution to a homogeneous system of equations will also be a solution.

6. Make a conjecture about the number of solutions that a homogeneous system of equations will have if it has at least one non-trivial solution.
Sample answer: it will have an infinite number of solutions.

NAME _____ DATE _____ PERIOD _____

3-5 Word Problem Practice

Solving Systems of Equations in Three Variables

1. **SIBLINGS** Amy, Karen, and Nolan are siblings. Their ages in years can be represented by the variables A, K, and N, respectively. They have lived a total of 22 years combined. Karen has lived twice as many years as Amy, and Nolan has lived 6 years longer than Amy. Use the equations $A + K + N = 22$, $K = 2A$, and $N = A + 6$ to find the age of each sibling.
Amy is 4, Karen is 8, and Nolan is 10.

2. **HOCKEY** Bobby Hull scored G goals, A assists, and P points in his NHL career. By definition, $P = G + A$. He scored 50 more goals than assists. Had he scored 15 more goals and 15 more assists, he would have scored 1200 points. How many goals, assists, and points did Bobby Hull score?
610 goals, 560 assists, and 1170 points

3. **EXERCISE** Larry, Camille, and Simone are keeping track of how far they walk each day. At the end of the week, they combined their distances and found that they had walked 34 miles in total. They also learned that Camille walked twice as far as Larry, and that Larry walked 2 more miles than Simone. How far did each person walk?
Camille walked 18 mi, Larry walked 9 mi, and Simone walked 7 mi.

DISTANCES For Exercises 4 and 5, use the following information.

Let c be the distance between Carlisle and Wellesley, let b be the distance between Carlisle and Stonebridge, and let a be the distance between Wellesley and Stonebridge.

- If you did a circuit, traveling from Carlisle to Wellesley to Stonebridge and back to Carlisle, you would travel 73 miles.
- Stonebridge is 12 miles farther than Wellesley is from Carlisle.
- If you drove from Stonebridge to Carlisle and back to Stonebridge, and then continued to Wellesley then back to Stonebridge, you would travel 102 miles.

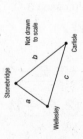

Stonebridge

a

b

Not drawn to scale

c

Wellesley

Carlisle

4. Write a system of linear equations to represent the situation.
1. $a + b + c = 73$
2. $b = c + 12$
3. $2a + 2b = 102$

5. Solve the system of equations. Explain the meaning of the solution in the context of the situation.
$a = 17$, $b = 34$, $c = 22$;
It is 17 miles from Wellesley to Stonebridge, 34 miles from Stonebridge to Carlisle, and 22 miles from Carlisle to Wellesley.

Chapter 3 Assessment Answer Key

Quiz 1 (Lessons 3-1 and 3-2)
Page 45

1.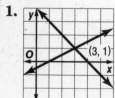

2.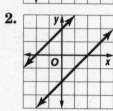

   inconsistent

3. **no solution;**
   inconsistent system

4. _____ **(−3, −2)** _____

5. _____ **B** _____

Quiz 2 (Lesson 3-3)
Page 45

1.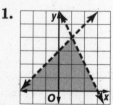

2.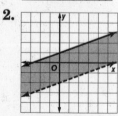

3. **(0, 0), (0, 4), (2, 0)**

4. **(1, −2), (2, 0),**
   (3, −1), (3, −2)

5. $x + y \leq 15$
   $10x + 15y \geq 150$

Quiz 3 (Lesson 3-4)
Page 46

1. **max: $f(1, 6) = 11$;**
   min: $f(1, −1) = −3$

2.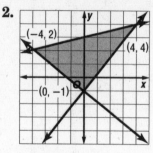

3. **vertices:**
   (−4, 2), (4, 4), (0, −1)

4. **max: $f(0, −1) = 5$;**
   min: $f(4, 4) = −16$

5. $j \geq 0, p \geq 0$
   $j + 2p \leq 20$
   $4j + 2p \leq 32$

Quiz 4 (Lesson 3-5)
Page 46

1. _____ **(−1, 2, −4)** _____

2. _____ **(2, 3, −1)** _____

3. _____ **(1, −2, 4)** _____

4. $x + y + z = 155,$
   $x = 9y, y = 3z$

5. **135 cars, 15 vans,**
   5 trucks

Mid-Chapter Test
Page 47

1. _____ **C** _____

2. _____ **H** _____

3. _____ **A** _____

4. _____ **F** _____

5.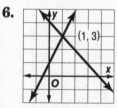

6.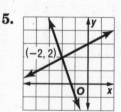

7. **consistent and**
   dependent

8.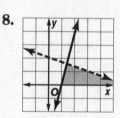

9. **(−2, 3), (−2, 6),**
   (0, 6), (4, 0)

(continued on the next page)

Chapter 3 Assessment Answer Key

Vocabulary Text
Page 48

1. inconsistent system
2. dependent system
3. ordered triple
4. substitution method
5. constraints
6. system of inequalities
7. elimination method
8. consistent system
9. system of equations
10. linear programming

11. Sample answer: In a linear programming problem, the region that is the intersection of the graphs of the constraints is called the feasible region.

12. Sample answer: When a system of linear inequalities is graphed, if the solutions form a region that is not a polygonal region, then we say the region is an unbounded region.

Form 1
Page 49

1. D
2. G
3. F
4. A
5. G
6. B
7. F
8. D
9. G
10. B
11. H

Page 50

12. A
13. G
14. C
15. J
16. B
17. H
18. A
19. G
20. A

B: 4 units^2

Chapter 3 Assessment Answer Key

Form 2A
Page 51

1. __B__

2. __G__

3. __H__

4. __D__

5. __H__

6. __A__

7. __H__

8. __A__

9. __J__

10. __D__

11. __H__

Page 52

12. __B__

13. __F__

14. __D__

15. __H__

16. __C__

17. __J__

18. __A__

19. __F__

20. __A__

B: __$\frac{9}{8}$__

Form 2B
Page 53

1. __A__

2. __F__

3. __H__

4. __A__

5. __G__

6. __B__

7. __F__

8. __D__

9. __J__

10. __D__

11. __G__

Page 54

12. __A__

13. __H__

14. __C__

15. __H__

16. __D__

17. __F__

18. __B__

19. __H__

20. __C__

B: __$a = 2, b = 4, c = 1, d = 3, f = 0$__

Chapter 3 Assessment Answer Key

Form 2C
Page 55

Page 56

1.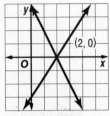

2.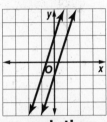

no solution

3. consistent and independent

4. consistent and dependent

5. $(4, 1)$

6. $(0, 4)$

7. $(2, 1)$

8. $(2, -2)$

9.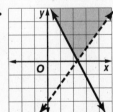

10.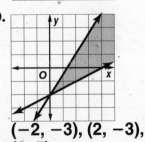

$(-2, -3), (2, -3),$
11. $(2, 5)$

$(-2, 0), (3, -5),$
12. $(3, 2), (0, 4)$

13. $(-2, -3), (-2, 9),$
$(2, 5)$

14. max: $f(2, 5) = 1$;
min: $f(-2, 9) = -15$

15. $c \geq 0, b \geq 0,$
$6c + 30b \leq 600,$
$c + b \leq 60$

16. 50 cars, 10 buses

17. $(0, 1, -1)$

18. $(-1, 2, 1)$

19. $s + m + \ell = 9$
$7s + 12m + 15\ell = 86$
$m = 3\ell$

20. 5 small packages,
3 medium packages,
1 large package

B: 20 units

Answers

Chapter 3 Assessment Answer Key

Form 2D
Page 57

Page 58

1.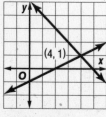

2.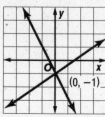

3. __inconsistent__

4. __consistent and independent__

5. __(4, 6)__

6. __(−2, −8)__

7. __(−1, 3)__

8. __(2, −2)__

9.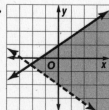

10.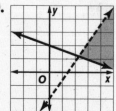

11. (−3, −2), (0, −2), (−3, 4)

12. (−1, −3), (−4, 0), (0, 3), (2, 3)

13. __(−5, 7), (1, 7), (−1, 3)__

14. max: $f(1, 7) = 10$; min: $f(−5, 7) = −8$

15. $l \geq 0, v \geq 4,$ $v + l \leq 15$

16. __$138__

17. __(−2, 3, 5)__

18. __(3, 1, −4)__

19. $w = 2h, t = h − 4,$ $3w + 2h + 5t = 136$

20. __$24__

B: __(12, −8)__

Chapter 3 Assessment Answer Key

Form 3
Page 59

1.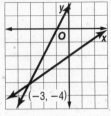

2.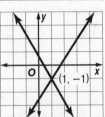

3. consistent and dependent

4. inconsistent

5. $(-2, 6)$

6. no solution

7. $\left(-3, \dfrac{1}{4}\right)$

8. $(1.5, -2)$

9.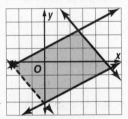

10.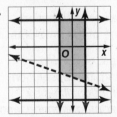

11. $(-6, 3), (2, 3),$ $(2, -4), (1, -4)$

12. $(-2, 4), (5, -3),$ $(5, -4), (1, -4),$ $(-2, 2)$

Page 60

13. $(-3, -4), (-3, 1),$ $(0, 4), (3, 2)$

14. max: $f(3, 2) = 8$; min: $f(-3, 1) = \dfrac{-19}{2}$

15. $60a + 150m \le 900,$ $a \ge 3, m \ge 4$

16. 5 ads and 4 commercial minutes; 124,000 people

17. $\left(\dfrac{1}{2}, -\dfrac{2}{3}, -5\right)$

18. $\left(\dfrac{1}{5}, -1, 21\right)$

19. $s = 3a, m = a - 10$ $15s + 40a + 5m$ $= 2650$

20. $90

B: $(6, 2)$

Answers

Chapter 3 Assessment Answer Key

Page 61, Extended-Response Test
Scoring Rubric

Score	General Description	Specific Criteria
4	**Superior** A correct solution that is supported by well-developed, accurate explanations	• Shows thorough understanding of the concepts of *solving systems of linear equations by graphing, by substitution, and by elimination; solving systems of inequalities by graphing; solving problems using linear programming;* and *solving systems in three variables.* • Uses appropriate strategies to solve problems. • Computations are correct. • Written explanations are exemplary. • Graphs are accurate and appropriate. • Goes beyond requirements of some or all problems.
3	**Satisfactory** A generally correct solution, but may contain minor flaws in reasoning or computation	• Shows an understanding of the concepts of *solving systems of linear equations by graphing, by substitution, and by elimination; solving systems of inequalities by graphing; solving problems using linear programming;* and *solving systems in three variables.* • Uses appropriate strategies to solve problems. • Computations are mostly correct. • Written explanations are effective. • Graphs are mostly accurate and appropriate. • Satisfies all requirements of problems.
2	**Nearly Satisfactory** A partially correct interpretation and/or solution to the problem	• Shows an understanding of most of the concepts of *solving systems of linear equations by graphing, by substitution, and by elimination; solving systems of inequalities by graphing; solving problems using linear programming;* and *solving systems in three variables.* • May not use appropriate strategies to solve problems. • Computations are mostly correct. • Written explanations are satisfactory. • Graphs are mostly accurate. • Satisfies the requirements of most of the problems.
1	**Nearly Unsatisfactory** A correct solution with no supporting evidence or explanation	• Final computation is correct. • No written explanations or work is shown to substantiate the final computation. • Graphs may be accurate but lack detail or explanation. • Satisfies minimal requirements of some of the problems.
0	**Unsatisfactory** An incorrect solution indicating no mathematical understanding of the concept or task, or no solution is given	• Shows little or no understanding of most of *solving systems of linear equations by graphing, by substitution, and by elimination; solving systems of inequalities by graphing; solving problems using linear programming;* and *solving systems in three variables.* • Does not use appropriate strategies to solve problems. • Computations are incorrect. • Written explanations are unsatisfactory. • Graphs are inaccurate or inappropriate. • Does not satisfy requirements of problems. • No answer may be given.

Chapter 3 Assessment Answer Key

Page 61, Extended-Response Test
Sample Answers

In addition to the scoring rubric found on page A26, the following sample answers may be used as guidance in evaluating open-ended assessment items.

1. Let J = Janet's age, K = Kim's age, and S = Sue's age.
   $J^2 = (K + S)^2 + 400$ and $K + S = J - 10$
   $J^2 = (J - 10)^2 + 400$
   $J^2 = J^2 - 20J + 100 + 400$
   $20J = 500$
   $J = 25$
   Thus, $K + S = 25 - 10$ or 15 and $J + (K + S) = 25 + 15$ or 40. Therefore, $(J + K + S)^2 = 40^2$ or 1600.

2a. $x \geq 0$
    $y \geq 0$
    $y \leq -\frac{4}{3}x + 8$

2b. Sample answer: Evaluate $f(x, y)$ at each of the vertices of the region.

3. Student responses should indicate that the solution of a system of equations is an ordered pair representing the point at which the graphs of the equations intersect. Solutions should include the fact that a system may have no solution, indicating that the graphs of the lines are parallel and that a system may have an infinite number of solutions, indicating that the equations represent the same line.

4. Student responses should indicate that it is impossible for a system to be both inconsistent (a system of non-intersecting lines) and dependent (a system of two representations of the same line).

5. Students should demonstrate an understanding that, if the graphs of the cost and revenue functions are parallel, the cost and revenue have the same rate of change. This means that the company will never break even on the production and sale of these products and, therefore, never make a profit. The owner may decide to increase the price charged for the product, may look for ways to cut costs, may put the company resources into the production of other products, or may even decide to close up shop.

6. Students should indicate that a system of two linear inequalities has no solution when there are no ordered pairs which satisfy both inequalities. Graphically, this means that the shaded regions which represent the graphs of the inequalities do not intersect. Students' graphs should show two parallel lines with shading everywhere but between them.
   Sample answer: $x \leq -3, x \geq 2$

Chapter 3 Assessment Answer Key

Standardized Test Practice

Page 62

1. Ⓐ Ⓑ Ⓒ Ⓓ

2. Ⓕ Ⓖ Ⓗ Ⓙ

3. Ⓐ Ⓑ Ⓒ Ⓓ

4. Ⓕ Ⓖ Ⓗ Ⓙ

5. Ⓐ Ⓑ Ⓒ Ⓓ

6. Ⓕ Ⓖ Ⓗ Ⓙ

7. Ⓐ Ⓑ Ⓒ Ⓓ

8. Ⓕ Ⓖ Ⓗ Ⓙ

9. Ⓐ Ⓑ Ⓒ Ⓓ

10. Ⓕ Ⓖ Ⓗ Ⓙ

Page 63

11. Ⓐ Ⓑ Ⓒ Ⓓ

12. Ⓕ Ⓖ Ⓗ Ⓙ

13. Ⓐ Ⓑ Ⓒ Ⓓ

14. Ⓕ Ⓖ Ⓗ Ⓙ

15. Ⓐ Ⓑ Ⓒ Ⓓ

16. **2 0 0**

17. **9**

Chapter 3 Assessment Answer Key

18. $-2x - 27$

19. $m = -3$

20. $\{x | x < -5 \text{ or } x > 2\}$ or $(-\infty, -5) \cup (2, +\infty)$

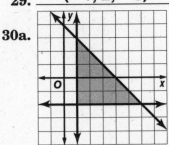

-6 -5 -4 -3 -2 -1 0 1 2 3

21. $-8a^3 + 4a - 5$

22. No, because the variable appears in a denominator.

23. No, because x has an exponent other than 1.

24. $y = -4x + 5$

25. $\dfrac{37}{8}$ or $4\dfrac{5}{8}$

26. consistent and independent

27. $(-4, -3)$

28. $(-1, 2)$

29. $(-1, 2, -3)$

30a.

30b. $(1, 3), (6, -2), (1, -2)$

30c. max: $f(1, 3) = 0$; min: $f(6, -2) = -20$